Scholastic Literacy Skills

Grammar and punctuation

AGES 10–11

TERM-BY-TERM PHOTOCOPIABLES

AUTHOR HUW THOMAS

With thanks to the children of Springfield School, Sheffield

EDITOR STEVEN CARRUTHERS

ASSISTANT EDITOR ROANNE DAVIS

SERIES DESIGNER CLAIRE BELCHER

ILLUSTRATIONS JANE ANDREWS

Designed using Adobe Pagemaker

Published by Scholastic Ltd, Villiers House, Clarendon Avenue, Leamington Spa, Warwickshire CV32 5PR
Text © Huw Thomas

© 1999 Scholastic Ltd

1 2 3 4 5 6 7 8 9 0   9 0 1 2 3 4 5 6

British Library Cataloguing-in-Publication Data
A catalogue record for this book is available from the British Library.

ISBN 0-590-63670-7

01926   887799   Fax   88333/

Acknowledgements
The publishers gratefully acknowledge permission to reproduce the following copyright material:
Rupert Crew Ltd for permission to reproduce extracts from 'Hands Up' and 'Fruity Fangs' from *The Trickster's Handbook* by Peter Eldin © 1976, Peter Eldin (1976, Fontana).
Dover Publications Inc, New York for 'The Princess on the Pea', changed to 'The Princess and the Pea' in this publication from *Yellow Fairy Book* by Andrew Lang (1998, Dover Publications).
Egmont Children's Books for the use of 'The Lamplighter's Funeral' from *Six Apprentices* by Leon Garfield © 1984, Leon Garfield (1984, Heinemann).
Faber & Faber for the use of an extract from *The Iron Man* by Ted Hughes © 1989, Ted Hughes (1989, Faber & Faber).
Ladybird Books for the use of an extract 'Fun with wool' reproduced from the former Ladybird title *Magnets and Electricity* © 1982, Ladybird Books Ltd (1982, Ladybird Books).

Every effort has been made to trace copyright holders for the works reproduced in this book, and the publishers apologize for any inadvertent omissions.

Contents

Introduction

Welcome to grammar and punctuation

'As a writer I know that I must select studiously the nouns, pronouns, verbs, adverbs, etcetera, and by a careful syntactical arrangement make readers laugh, reflect or riot.'

Maya Angelou

The *Scholastic Literacy Skills: Grammar and punctuation* series equips teachers with resources and subject training enabling them to teach grammar and punctuation at Key Stage 2. The focus of the resource is on what is sometimes called *sentence-level* work, so called because grammar and punctuation primarily involve the construction and understanding of sentences.

Many teachers approach the teaching of grammar bringing with them a lot of past memories. Some will remember school grammar lessons as the driest of subjects, involving drills and parsing, and will wonder how they can make it exciting for their own class. At the other end of the spectrum, some will have received relatively little formal teaching of grammar at school. Recent research by the Qualifications and Curriculum Authority found a lack of confidence among Key Stage 2 teachers when it came to teaching sentence structure, commenting that:

'Where teachers were less confident, it tended to be because sentence structure had not formed part of their own education.'

(QCA, 1998, page 28)

In other words there are teachers who, when asked to teach clause structure or prepositions, feel at a bit of a loss. They are being asked to teach things they are not confident with themselves. Even worse, they think they should be confident in these things.

Grammar can evoke lethargy, fear, irritation, pedantry and despondency. Yet at the beginning of this introduction we have one of the greatest modern writers presenting her crafting of sentences as an exciting and tactical process that has a powerful effect on her readers. Can this be the grammar that makes teachers squirm or run?

The *Scholastic Literacy Skills: Grammar and punctuation* series

The *Scholastic Literacy Skills: Grammar and punctuation* series works from the premise that grammar and punctuation can be interesting and dynamic – but on one condition. The condition is that the teaching of these aspects of grammar must be related to *real texts* and *practical activities* that experiment with language, investigate the use of language in real contexts and find the ways in which grammar and punctuation are used in our day-to-day talk, writing and reading. The series is based upon five principles about the teaching of grammar:

1. Meaningful sentence-level work
In looking at how sentences are put together in a text, an appreciation of the function of that text is crucial. As children investigate the structure of sentences or the types of words they contain, they need to be aware of them as communicative acts; the purposes of the various pieces of writing considered in this resource play a crucial role in the activities. As children work through various aspects of *Grammar and punctuation*, teachers should reflect on how individual children are using their developing understanding of sentences in the rest of their written and spoken work.

2. Language from real life
As far as is possible, children need to work with language set in real-life contexts rather than always looking at contrived texts and exercises. Instead of made-up newspapers, for example, they need to look at extracts from the real thing. They need the encouragement to look at language in their environment, the books they enjoy and the things they and their peers say to one another. These are some of the most valuable resources available for language work because in using them children will apply what they learn to texts they know.

Introduction

The *Scholastic Literacy Skills: Grammar and punctuation* series does contain a number of exercises in which sentences have been constructed purely to provide examples of the use of a particular type of word or punctuation mark. However, this is always complemented by more realistic uses of language. The aim is consistently to refer children to genuine texts extracted from real books and actual newspapers. For this reason the *Scholastic Literacy Skills: Grammar and punctuation* series asks children to work on grammar and punctuation using texts as diverse as fables, jokes, book blurbs, leaflets, children's own writing, comic stories, poems, scripts, comedy sketches, labels, classic poetry, texts in various dialects… in fact the mix is as rich and lively as the children's own language experiences should be. A flick through the photocopiable material in this book will show the commitment of the series to varied and interesting texts based on the conviction that relevant and appropriate texts will motivate children to learn about language.

3. Teachers as active participants

The 'rules' of grammar and punctuation are not static aspects of language; we are all continually revising and developing them. The most competent and experienced of writers can still find new and interesting features of these aspects of language and develop their own use of English. Because of this the *Scholastic Literacy Skills: Grammar and punctuation* series equips the teacher with subject knowledge, definitions and explanations as

preparation for the subject matter of each unit. It is important that, as far as is possible, teachers join in with activities. If, for example, an activity involves bringing a leaflet in from home and looking at the use of persuasive language, then everyone should take part. What many teachers have found is that grammar and punctuation can be great levellers. In other words, as children investigate these aspects of language, the teacher can join in and genuinely participate in developing his or her own use of English.

4. Structure is essential

While the *Scholastic Literacy Skills: Grammar and punctuation* series is full of interesting and lively material, it is underpinned by a clear and deliberate structure. The sentence-level aspects of English are so many and so varied that teaching them effectively demands a structured approach. The basic aim has been to provide a clearly structured resource that uses common sense and introduces features such as sentence structure and punctuation in ways that build continuity and progression into children's learning.

The half-term sections and units of each book are structured in a way that develops the teaching of grammar and punctuation in Key Stage 2 in England, Wales and Northern Ireland, and Levels C–E in Scotland. Care has been taken to encompass the National Literacy Strategy *Framework for Teaching* (DfEE, 1998), so that teachers following the strategy can use these books with the confidence that they are delivering all the appropriate sentence-level objectives for each year group.

5. Active enjoyment

This is not a book of basic drills. The *Scholastic Literacy Skills: Grammar and punctuation* series was put together in the knowledge that grammar and punctuation *can* be taught in a dry and dull way but with a commitment to do the complete opposite. With this in mind, the activities are constructed in a way that involves a lot of active investigative work and play with language.

The books provide a balanced 'diet' of exercises mixed with practical, hands-on activities, including researching language, recording and analysing speech, drama activities, games and advertising. The underlying premise is that language is interesting, that understanding it can be fascinating and that working with it can be fun.

Grammar and punctuation: do they matter?

Any introduction to the teaching of grammar and punctuation sets up a stall in the middle of one of the hottest debates in the teaching of English. For this reason it is necessary to say a few things about the usefulness and purpose of sentence-level teaching.

Background

There was a period from the 1960s to the 1980s when the teaching of grammar in particular and punctuation to a lesser extent was not in vogue. This was, in part, due to research projects in the 1960s that claimed to have shown the teaching of such aspects of English to be 'useless' and even 'harmful' (for example, Harris's research summarized in QCA, 1998). The Kingman Report in 1988 marked a change in this situation. After a period in which grammar had lain dormant, this report promoted the use of grammatical terminology in relevant contexts and recommended that all trainee teachers receive a large amount of 'direct tuition of knowledge about language' (HMSO, 1988, page 69).

A large portion of the Kingman Report was devoted to considering the talk and work of children. These were examined and the implicit linguistic knowledge in these activities was drawn out, such as the six-year-old whose writing demonstrated implicit understanding of subordinate clauses and qualifying phrases (HMSO, 1988, page 36). Taking the example of discussion about pronouns they made a comment that:

'Since… teacher and pupil need, in discussion, a word which refers to a class of terms (i.e. pronouns) there is no good reason not to use that term.'

(HMSO, 1988, page 13)

What Kingman raised was the usefulness of knowledge about language in the teaching of English.

Reasons for teaching grammar and punctuation

Grammar and punctuation are sometimes seen as symbols of a golden age when children were taught 'the basics'. This sort of talk has not served the subject well. It took some time for the Kingman recommendations to permeate into the English curriculum in a thorough and progressive way. It is crucial that, as teachers embark on the teaching of grammar and punctuation, they do so with a clear sense of exactly what it is these subjects will provide the learner with. The *Scholastic Literacy Skills: Grammar and punctuation* series is based on the following theoretical understanding of the value of teaching grammar and punctuation.

❑ Understanding and using terminology used to describe aspects of grammar and punctuation equips children with the vocabulary they need to discuss language. For example, it can be much easier to discuss the ambiguities that can surround the use of pronouns with children if they understand the term 'pronoun' and are beginning to use it to describe some of the words they use.

❑ Looking at aspects of sentence construction stimulates children to reflect on their own use of language. For example, many teachers try to discourage the overuse of the word 'and…' as in 'I went out and I saw my friend and we played in the park and we went to the shop and we bought…' and so on. Guiding children out of this overuse of 'and' is a task with which many teachers are familiar. It can be greatly enhanced by an understanding of certain aspects of grammar and punctuation such as how sentences break up a piece of writing so that it makes sense; other words and terms that can connect sentences and clauses together; ways in which sentences and clauses can be punctuated; and the functions performed by specific connecting words and phrases.

❑ There are links within the subject of English that make one aspect vital to the understanding of another. For example, the understanding of how certain texts address and persuade their readers involves an awareness of the concept of 'person' in pronouns and verbs. Another example is the way in which the use of the comma can depend on an understanding of how clauses function. Many aspects of grammar and punctuation play vital roles in other areas of English.

❑ Grammar and punctuation can provide a means of evaluating how effectively and clearly a spoken or written piece of language communicates. For example, the teacher who is exasperated by a child's constant use of the word 'nice' to describe everything he or she likes might find some work on adjectives steers the child towards new ways of describing.

❑ An appreciation of grammar and punctuation empowers children to make full use of the English language. Starting with simple sentences, children can move on to an understanding of features such as nouns, verbs, commas, clauses, adjectives and adverbs. Grammar and punctuation become the tools that enable children to explore new ways of expressing themselves in their writing.

Introduction

Linguistics, the study of language, is a subject in its own right. Looking at grammar and punctuation gives children their first encounters with this fascinating subject. The discussion of language features such as dialect words and expressions introduces children to the subject of sociolinguistics. This is the study of how language functions within society and it is just one example of the way in which the study of language can be an interesting subject in itself.

Working with *Scholastic Literacy Skills: Grammar and punctuation*

Unit structure

Each book in the *Scholastic Literacy Skills: Grammar and punctuation* series is broken up into six sections, each of which is structured to provide resources for a half-term. Within each section, material is gathered together to give a specific content to that half-term, indicated on the contents page. Each section contains two 'posters' that present some of the material covered over the half-term in an accessible form for reference. These are so named because it is recommended that they are enlarged to A3 size (or A2, using two A3 sheets) and placed on display while the units are undertaken. They can also be used as shared texts in reading activities as well as posters provided for reference in the classroom.

Each half-term section is split into five units, each dealing with a specific aspect of grammar or punctuation. Within each unit there are three photocopiables. These are prefaced by introductory material, structured under the following headings:

Objective: the learning objective(s) for the unit.

Language issues: explanatory material on the issues covered in the unit. These are predominantly focused on the subject matter of the unit and can provide clarification for the teacher, equipping him or her towards delivery of the unit.

Ways of teaching: notes on the teaching of the subject matter. This section can provide specific points about the approach to be adopted and the terminology to be used, and has a specific bearing upon the teaching of the unit.

About the activities: a note that clarifies any information the teacher may need for the unit. In some cases this is a full explanation of the activity; in others it is just a hint on the presentation of the subject matter.

Following up: optional activity suggestions to follow up the content of the unit. These can be specific activities but they can also be notes as to how the content of the unit can dovetail with other aspects of English.

Differentiation

The activities in each book are produced with the average ability of the relevant year group in mind. They draw upon the work of the National Literacy Project, a pilot project that led to the production of the National Literacy Strategy (DfEE, 1998). Differentiation should be possible within each unit in the following ways:

Providing support in the way activities are staged. When, for example, there are three stages to an activity, the teacher can assist children who need support through one or more of the stages.

Reducing the amount of material. If an activity asks children to complete a certain number of tasks, such as the ordering of ten mixed-up sentences, the teacher may reduce the number for a child needing such support.

Pre-selecting appropriate material for investigative tasks. Many of the units ask children to find texts or try activities with sentences they find in the classroom. In such cases the teacher could direct children who would find this difficult to specified sentences or previously selected material.

Providing follow-up work. More able children can benefit from being given one of the tasks under the heading 'Following up', extending their work based on the objective of the unit.

A 'resource', not a 'scheme'

The photocopiables in each book are a support for teaching. While they may carry notes to inform children, the actual teaching of the learning objective can only be achieved through discussion of the language issues supported by the use of the photocopiable sections. This takes us back to the idea of the teacher as an active participant. These materials are to be used by the class working in conjunction with the teacher and should support the teacher's explanation and discussion of the subject matter in each unit.

It should be stressed that *Scholastic Literacy Skills: Grammar and punctuation* does not intend to provide a scheme that children slavishly work their way through. It is a flexible teaching resource. While each book provides the subject matter appropriate to the age group at which it is aimed, the teacher will soon realize there is more material in each book than a class could be expected to cover in one year. The introductory pages at the start of each half-termly section and the language issues sections are there to enable teachers to select the photocopiable page, poster, or activity from the 'Following up' section, that best supports their own planning, the needs of the class – and personal preferences.

Texts, texts and more texts!
Various activities call for a range of resources. Check each activity to see what is needed in the way of paper, scissors, glue and so on. The most valuable resource, however, is a rich variety of texts available for the children's use – collect together a truly mixed bag of old and new texts (familiar and unfamiliar), including leaflets, menus, newspapers, comics, letters, junk mail, posters… the broader the range the better!

Introduction to Ages 10–11
The thirty units comprising *Scholastic Literacy Skills: Grammar and punctuation, Ages 10–11* have as their objective a consolidation of various aspects of grammar and punctuation to which children will already have been introduced (such as the different classes of word, and the active and passive forms of the verb) as well as an exploration of new subject matter such as types of clause, conditionals and modal verbs. These are vital aspects of the child's knowledge of language.

These units also reinforce work on punctuation that has been previously introduced, such as colons and semicolons. The book also looks at parentheses, as used with commas, dashes and brackets.

For this age group, children are also encouraged to investigate how changes at sentence-level (such as the different sorts of connectives and prepositions) influence the overall sense of language. The book concludes by examining the conventions and grammatical features of various genres of text, and encourages the children to undertake detailed investigations into different uses of language.

Word classes

Contents of Term 1a

This half-term

The units in this half-term are devoted to basic revision of classes of word. Children identify different types of word through a variety of activities. They then look at the way in which key changes are made in words within a particular grammatical category, including changing singular to plural in nouns and changes of tense in verbs. The unit avoids identifying one set of words as 'nouns', another as 'verbs' and so on, and focuses instead upon the functions of words in a particular context, bearing in mind the fact that words like 'sweet' can function in a variety of ways depending upon the context.

Poster notes

General grammar rules
This poster presents definitions of some of the main classes of word. The definitions are very basic and are intended as an *aide-mémoire* for children as they engage in the activities throughout the unit.

Alternative adjectives and adverbs
As a means of developing their use of adjectives and adverbs, this poster provides children with a range of both, upon which they could draw in their writing. Within each 'cluster' there is a range of adjectives and adverbs that could substitute for each other, depending upon the context.

General grammar rules

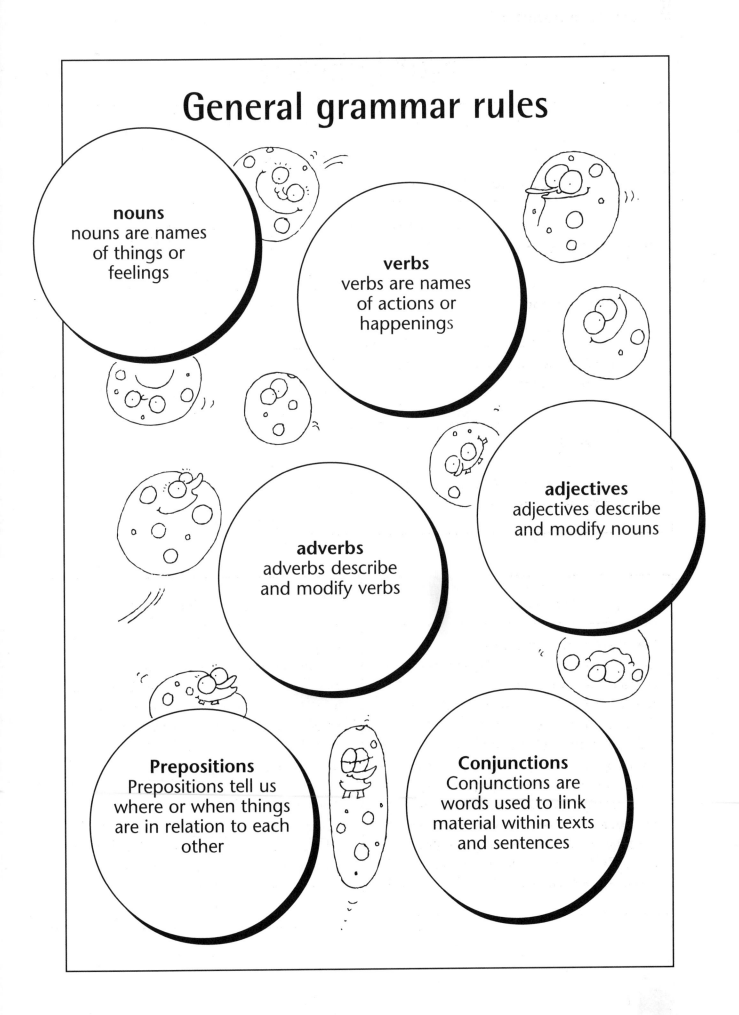

nouns
nouns are names of things or feelings

verbs
verbs are names of actions or happenings

adjectives
adjectives describe and modify nouns

adverbs
adverbs describe and modify verbs

Prepositions
Prepositions tell us where or when things are in relation to each other

Conjunctions
Conjunctions are words used to link material within texts and sentences

Alternative adjectives

best	useless	scary	slow
good	bad	frightening	lugubrious
better	awful	creepy	sluggish
brilliant	lousy	weird	leisurely
fantastic	terrible	eerie	lazy
excellent	nasty	chilling	

happy	sad	fast
jolly	miserable	quick
cheerful	gloomy	speedy
merry	glum	swift
pleased	disconsolate	rapid
delighted	unhappy	

Alternative adverbs

quickly	slowly	well
rapidly	lugubriously	brilliantly
swiftly	sluggishly	correctly
hurriedly	cautiously	properly
briskly	lazily	successfully

badly	angrily
shoddily	madly
poorly	viciously
unsatisfactorily	wildly

Revision of word classes

Objective
Revise different word classes

Language issues
Nouns and verbs are two of the most common types of word encountered in English. Defined basically, nouns are words that denote things. They denote objects, people, places and emotions. They name the things in a sentence, so in a sentence like 'The dog barked', the noun is 'dog'.

Verbs denote actions or happenings. In the same sentence the verb is 'barked'.

Adjectives describe nouns. They are the words or phrases that modify a noun, providing more information about the thing denoted in the noun. The adjective 'fierce' could be inserted in the sentence quoted above to create 'The fierce dog barked'. Adverbs perform a similar function in relation to verbs. They modify them. In the above example the word 'loudly' could be inserted: 'The dog barked loudly'.

Ways of teaching
There are exceptions to many of the rules in grammar. However the value of basic definitions cannot be avoided. It is hard to teach sentence structure without having a basic idea of what constitutes a verb. In this unit children renew their acquaintance with the four basic parts of speech examined in earlier years.

About the activities
Photocopiable: Wordsorts
Through using the sets on this photocopiable children can group together examples of words performing certain functions in sentences. They should be encouraged to do this with a range of texts, setting out with the purpose of finding examples of the various word classes.

Photocopiable: Words doing jobs
This activity follows on from 'wordsorts' providing sentences that can be used to find examples to place in each grouping. The sentence types are deliberately varied, changing the length and style of examples.

Photocopiable: Word inserts
Adverbs and adjectives modify verbs and nouns. The sentences in this activity work without being modified but it can demonstrate the way in which modifiers can add to a piece of writing. The adjective and adverb poster provides a resource to refer to in this activity.

Following up
Word changes: Children can look at sentences in texts, such as stories, and see which words they could change. Could they find a better word than one of the ones used? Could they be more descriptive? They could add to this activity the challenge of thinking about how easy it is to change certain types of words without altering the underlying meaning of the sentence. Are verbs easier to change than nouns?

Word colours: Children can find newspaper articles and comic stories and try shading over different word types in different colours. If they work with a partner there will be the added discussion of some of the choices thrown up by this activity.

Wordsorts

❑ Look at some sentences in

| a story | an article | a brochure | or another text. |

❑ Find words doing the jobs labelling these boxes.
Copy the words into the boxes.

nouns nouns are names of things or feelings	**verbs** verbs are names of actions or happenings
adjectives adjectives describe and modify nouns	**adverbs** adverbs describe and modify verbs

Words doing jobs

❑ Cut out and look at these sentences.

The fierce dog barked loudly.

The monster was scary and it suddenly leaped out of the cave.

In the old cupboard there is a dusty chest.

The girl angrily kicked the can over the tall fence.

When you pass the sleeping dog, creep quietly.

Take your little sister to nursery and quickly return to class.

Is this dress too scruffy?

Speak politely!

Some of the words in these sentences can be sorted into the sets on the 'Wordsorts' chart.

❑ Cut out words that can be sorted into wordsorts boxes.

Word Insert

❑ Cut out these sentence strips.

❑ Split them in places where you could add an adjective or adverb.

| 'I walked to the house'. | 'I | walked to the | house'. |

❑ Cut out small strips of paper. Make some inserts. Use these to add adjectives and adverbs. Try to use unusual ones.

| 'I | carefully | walked to the | creepy | house'. |

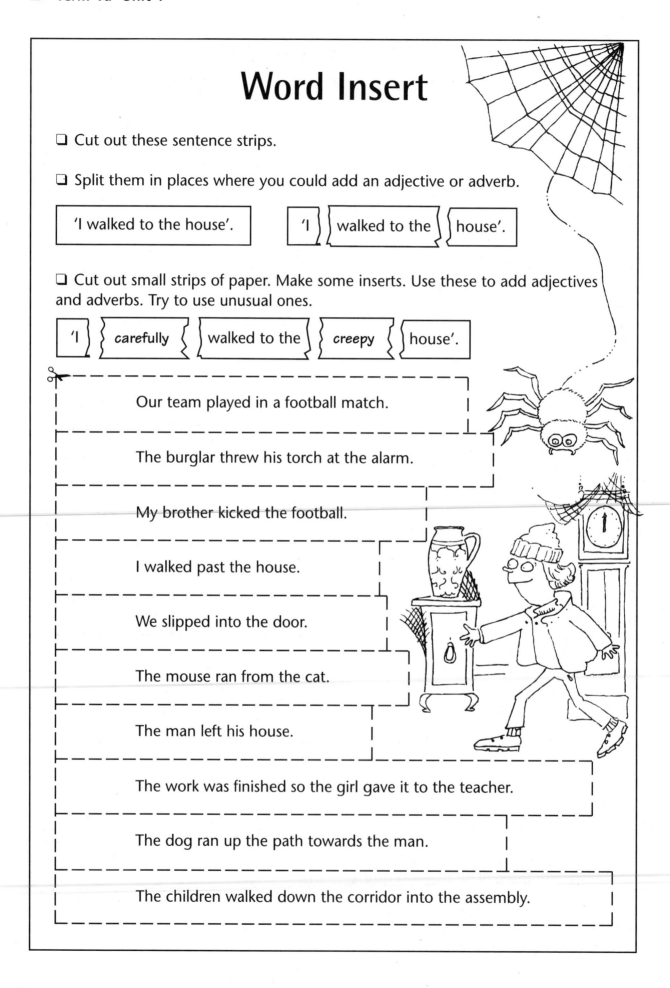

Our team played in a football match.

The burglar threw his torch at the alarm.

My brother kicked the football.

I walked past the house.

We slipped into the door.

The mouse ran from the cat.

The man left his house.

The work was finished so the girl gave it to the teacher.

The dog ran up the path towards the man.

The children walked down the corridor into the assembly.

Further revision

Objective
Further revision of different word classes

Language issues
Moving beyond basic definitions of nouns and verbs there are certain ways in which certain word classes behave. These are essential to the effective use of words in these classes but they also provide a way of classifying different types of word.

Nouns can be plural or singular. The single denotes one of something, the plural denotes more than one, for example:
dog   dogs.

Certain nouns do not usually appear in their plural form. This is particularly true of abstract nouns such as 'happiness' and 'joy' that are used to denote feelings. However, they can be and sometimes are pluralized, for example:
the joys of parenting
the miseries of parenting!

Verbs can alter their tense. A verb can appear in the present tense, such as 'I run', and in the past tense – 'I ran'. Verb phrases can also be constructed to express the future tense of a verb, though this usually involves the use of another verb such as 'will' or 'shall', as in 'I will run'.

Ways of teaching
Pluralization and tense change provide two ways of identifying nouns and verbs in sentences. If a word can be taken from singular to plural or vice versa it is a noun. This is useful when identifying words that usually function as verbs, such as 'walk', functioning as nouns, such as 'We had many enjoyable walks'. Similarly the change of tense can be a way of identifying verbs. If a sentence set in the present is remodelled in the past the words that change tense will be the verbs, for example
'I run and catch the bus'
I ran and caught the bus'.

About the activities
Photocopiable: Singular and plural
As children change the sentences from singular to plural they will need to decide which words make the transition. In doing this they are applying one of the ways of identifying nouns and performing one of the main grammatical operations that can be done with these verbs. The activity will also revise some of the irregularities of spelling involved in this change.

Photocopiable: Tense
The three groupings contain different types of words. Some use participles within compound tenses, where two or more words make up the verb – for example, I was learning... Children should be encouraged to focus upon the time at which an activity occurred, in the past or the future.

Photocopiable: Noun and verb match
From the various words provided on the photocopiable children need to sort out compound sentences, using the sentence format provided. They may create sentences that make sense or nonsense sentences.

Following up
Total tense: Children can try reading a paragraph in a different tense. If it is in the past they can try reading it as if it happened in the future. As they do this they can look at which words they need to alter, the alterations they make and how the new versions of these words sound. What changes would these involve in the spelling of these words?

Ping-Pong: In pairs children can say singular or plural nouns to their partner who has to quickly reply with the alternative. So if child A says 'Box', child B responds with 'Boxes'. Child B must then quickly think of a different noun. If played at speed this can result in children responding to words with new versions of the plural, such as when 'child' is met by 'childses'! When such weird examples occur it can be interesting to look at which pluralization rule is actually being followed.

Singular and plural

This sentence uses singular nouns.

| The cat chased the dog. |

It can be changed to contain plural nouns.

| The cats chased the dogs. |

The nouns are changed to make the singular words into plural words.

❑ Try changing these sentences from singular to plural or plural to singular.

Singular	Plural
The boy tidied the cupboard.	
My friend played with my game.	
	The clowns ate the flowers.
	Can the girls find the books?
	The children found the pencils.
Our teacher tested the switch.	
Your brother hid your sandwich.	

Tense

❑ Sort these sentences into   ones that happen in the present
ones that happened in the past
ones that will happen in the future.

❑ What do you notice about the different words in each group?

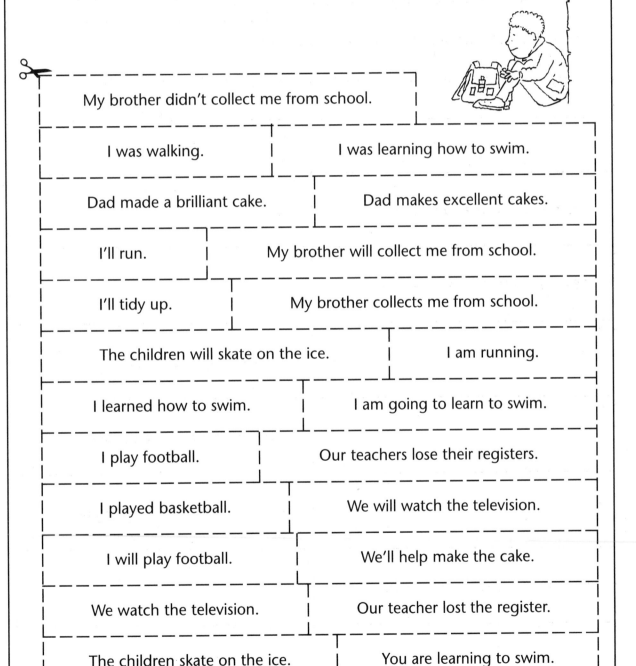

My brother didn't collect me from school.

I was walking.	I was learning how to swim.
Dad made a brilliant cake.	Dad makes excellent cakes.
I'll run.	My brother will collect me from school.
I'll tidy up.	My brother collects me from school.
The children will skate on the ice.	I am running.
I learned how to swim.	I am going to learn to swim.
I play football.	Our teachers lose their registers.
I played basketball.	We will watch the television.
I will play football.	We'll help make the cake.
We watch the television.	Our teacher lost the register.
The children skate on the ice.	You are learning to swim.

Noun and verb match

❑ Using nouns and verbs from the boxes below try making sentences with this structure.

The | **frog** | **croaked** | and the | **policewoman** | **applauded**

frog	applauded	audience	burglar
chased	cheered	chirped	cockerel
crickets	croaked	crowd	crowed
farmer	ocean	policewoman	ran
rocked	sang	scored	ship
singer	striker	swelled	woke up

❑ Write out some of the strange sentences you can make. Use a separate sheet of paper if you need to.

_____

_____

_____

_____

Prepositions and conjunctions

Objective
Further revision of different word classes, including prepositions and conjunctions.

Language issues
Prepositions are words or phrases that indicate where something is in relation to something else. They are, as the word implies, position words that come before other words. They usually appear before a noun or a pronoun. In a sentence like 'The cow jumped over the moon' the preposition explains where the cow was in relation to the moon, jumping 'over' as opposed to 'under' or 'through' it. There is a limited number of prepositions in the English language. A survey of words added to the language will show a growth in certain word types such as nouns and verbs. The number of prepositions, on the other hand, tends not to grow.

Conjunctions are words used to link material within texts and sentences. Conjunctions are used to join ('conjoin') two words, phrases or sentences together. The word 'and' is the most common conjunction, joining words:
'Joe made tea and coffee and juice'
or phrases:
'Joe made hot, sweet tea and much-needed coffee and his mum's home-made recipe for orange juice'
or sentences:
'Joe made tea. And later he cleaned up as well'.

Ways of teaching
As with the previous two units this one involves looking at the functions performed by certain types of word. The emphasis upon 'the job the word is doing' is essential to a child's understanding of these word classes.

About the activities
Photocopiable: Preposition picture
The picture prompts children to root out some of the prepositions they already know. They may come up with enough variety without the prompting. Children could try the same activity with other pictures.

Photocopiable: Preposition diary
This activity revises the use of prepositions to place things temporally. The children can try and use each of the examples shown.

Photocopiable: Conjunction selection
As children use the conjunctions they may notice that some of these words also function as prepositions. As conjunctions these words are introducing subordinate clauses.

Children could try finding spaces that could be filled by more than one of the conjunctions. They could also try to find which of the conjunctions listed has the potential to fill the greatest number of spaces.

Following up
Examples around us: Children can look around the room for examples of situations that can be described using a preposition, such as 'chair on the table'. This can be a way of amassing a number of prepositions. It can also be a challenge to children to find examples in which they can use particular prepositions. The teacher could ask a question like, 'Can anyone find a situation that would use the preposition "besides"?'

Conjunction day: Children can talk through events of a day using as many conjunctions as they can think of, as in 'I went to the cloakroom because I forgot my dinner money'.

Preposition picture

❏ Look at this picture and write some sentences about it.
Try using these words in your sentences.

up	into	out of	away from	between
across	in front of	about	through	against
after	towards	down	behind	under

Preposition diary

Prepositions tell us   where things are in relation to each other
when things happened in relation to each other.

❏ Using these prepositions write a diary of your day. Think of something that happened before something else, or after something else.

For example

| 'I did exercises before breakfast' | 'During the news I tidied the room' | 'After tea I played outside' | I played outside for half the afternoon' |

Prepositions to use:

| while | before | since | after | for | during | while | around | until |

Conjunction selection

❑ Look at these sentences and choose the word that can connect the two clauses.

We put the present _____ we knew mum wouldn't look.

We stayed in at playtime _____ it was too cold to go outside.

The bus driver started _____ we were sitting down.

My uncle was supposed to come to tea _____ he was too ill.

We went to town shopping _____ went to a cafe.

My friend is coming to stay _____ we put up a camp bed.

The fire bell rang _____ it was broken.

I had to stay in _____ I hadn't finished my work.

We wanted to play outside _____ it was raining.

It was mum's birthday _____ we made a cake.

Conjunctions							
and	before	but	however	because	so	then	where

Try to use each of the conjunctions at least once.

Word classes

Objective
Further revision of different word classes

Language issues
Words perform different functions. A word like 'kick'. cannot be simply labelled 'a verb'. Different words can perform different functions, depending on the context in which they are used. A word like 'kick' can be a verb in 'Kick the ball' and a noun in 'Give the ball a kick'. By looking at the definitions of the functions of various classes of words it is possible to decide which words are functioning as nouns, adjectives and so on depending upon the context.

Ways of teaching
When it comes to teaching, the observation of the function of words is critical. Words cannot be listed as 'nouns' or 'verbs'. They can perform a range of functions.

About the activities
Photocopiable: Word function
The passages in this activity have been selected to provide text extracts using varied word types, though through looking at them children may gain an idea of which word types are more common than others. Once they have sorted the words picked out in the activity they could go on to find other examples of each word class.

Photocopiable: Word type choosing
The object of this activity isn't so much to guess the missing word as to guess what type of word it could be. Children have to ask what job could be done by a word in that context. Once they have completed this they may like to create an example of their own to set others, drawing upon the different types of word function they have encountered.

Photocopiable: Nonsense grammar
Using the sentence guide in this photocopiable children generate various nonsensical sentences. Once they are used to the activity they can add some words of their own and see how these feature in various sentences.

Following up
Function box: The function box used in 'Word function' can be used in other texts. Children can also use it as a way of looking at which types of word are more common in certain texts. A poem may use more descriptive language than a football report.

Illustrate the nonsense: Once they have generated various nonsense sentences children can select a couple of their more absurd examples and draw illustrations for them.

Word function

❑ Look at the words underlined in these extracts.
❑ List the: nouns   verbs
              adjectives   adverbs
              prepositions   conjunctions

Possul <u>gazed</u> at the lamplighter, whose flame-lit countenance resembled an <u>angry</u> planet in the gloom; <u>then</u> his eyes strayed to <u>Pallcat's</u> lamps that <u>winked</u> in the <u>obscure</u> air <u>down</u> either side of the Strand. It took sharp eyes to make them out, they glimmered so <u>feebly</u> within the accumulated filth of the glass that <u>enclosed</u> them. Although they complied with the letter of the law and burned from <u>sunset</u> to sunrise, they <u>mocked</u> the <u>spirit</u> of the law and provided not the smallest scrap of illumination. If ever a world <u>walked</u> in need of light, it was the world under Pallcat's <u>lamps</u>.

Leon Garfield: The Lamplighter's Funeral

Hands Up:
<u>Get</u> a friend to stand in a doorway <u>and</u> to push the backs of his hands against the door frame as <u>hard</u> as he can. Keep him there <u>for</u> at least a minute and make sure that he is pushing hard all the time.

   Now tell him to <u>relax</u> the pressure and move away from the door. As he <u>does</u> so both of his <u>hands</u> will rise in the air <u>as if</u> pulled by <u>invisible</u> strings.

Peter Eldin: The Trickster's Handbook

nouns	verbs	adjectives	adverbs	prepositions	conjunctions

Word type choosing

❏ Look at this passage. What type of word could be used in each space? Suggest actual words that could fill the spaces.

My [a] was in the teacher's desk but I had to get it back so I did a [b] thing. I tried to steal it back. After school I [c] in the playground [d] all the teachers left. It was a [e] day and I shivered. I waited and waited [f]. When they had all gone I crept [g] through the door and [h] the classroom. I opened the desk [i] suddenly heard someone coming so I [j] hid under the table. It was the caretaker. He was a [k] bloke and I didn't want to cross him. He looked around [l] switched the lights off and [m] the door. I suddenly realised I was locked in this [n] building.

	type of word	my suggestion
a		
b		
c		
d		
e		
f		
g		
h		
i		
j		
k		
l		
m		
n		

Nonsense grammar

❑ Cut words from the boxes below and place them on the sentence maker.
See what strange sentences you can cook up! Make a note of the best ones.

The | **silly** | **policeman** | **chased** | the | **married** | **mouse**

above	red	policeman	sausage	sad
bit	viciously	silly	parrot	married
happily	posh	princess	toilet	broken
ate	voraciously	tasty	mouse	chased
threw	mangled			

RED BARRON

Complex sentences

Objective
Revise the construction of complex sentences

Language issues
Complex sentences are made up of more than one distinct section called clauses. If a sentence states:
The cat sat on the mat,
it gives a simple verbal description of where the cat performed the act of sitting. It could be extended to create a more complex sentence, such as:
'Before eating its owner, the cat sat on the mat, scratching it to shreds with those razor like claws'.
In this example there are more clauses providing more information. More clauses result in compound sentences. These are sentences containing clauses of equal importance, linked with connecting words like 'and' or 'then', for example:
'I had a coffee and my friend had a cake'.
Complex sentence use connecting words that subordinate one clause to another, making one the explanation of another, with words like 'because' and 'therefore', for example:
'I had a coffee because I was waiting for the bus'.

Ways of teaching
The complexity of sentences is a classic feature of the development of children's writing. From the basic single statement of writing children begin to develop more complex sentences in which ideas are combined and depend upon each other. When revising this children should look towards varying the sentence structure in their own writing.

About the activities
Photocopiable: Clauses
This activity asks children to find the clauses in sentences. The sentences provide some fairly clear cut examples of complex and compound sentences and, as children work through the activity, they can check each other's results to see how consistent their answers are.

Photocopiable: Linking and inserting clauses
Extra clauses can provide extra information in a sentence. This activity involves children in the task of reading the extra information and figuring out how they can use clauses to insert the extra information.

Photocopiable: Constructing complex
Once again the aspect of grammar in this unit only makes real sense when applied to actual texts children will encounter around them. This selection from *The Iron Man* has been chosen because of the interesting clause structure children will encounter within the text.

Following up
Complex practice: Children can practice producing complex sentences on a whiteboard or sheet of paper shared by a group. This activity provides a shared opportunity for children to look at the ways in which they can alter sentences and add extra information and clauses.

Clause shading: As with the extract from *The Iron Man* children can look at texts and try finding some of the clauses contained in the sentences. They can then shade over these in different colours.

Clauses

Clauses are distinct parts of a sentence. They have their own verb.
They are like a little sentence in themselves.
Some short sentences are made up of just one clause:

'The cat barked'.

Longer sentences have more than one clause

'The cat barked } and } the dog was surprised'.

Clauses can be linked by connectives.
❑ Look at these sentences and cut out the separate clauses.

The cat sang and the dog played the piano.

The dog was surprised because the cat started singing.

The dog used ear plugs so he couldn't hear the cat.

The cat got angry and she sang louder.

The dog caught a train however the cat followed him.

The dog hid in the luggage coach where the cat couldn't find him.

The dog got off at the station then the cat saw him.

The dog caught the next train before the cat could follow him.

The cat gave up singing and she became a pianist.

The dog became a train driver and he gave up the piano.

Linking and inserting clauses

Clauses can provide more information in a sentence.

❑ Look at this sentence.

> Mum likes a cup of tea.

Here is another piece of information that could go in the sentence.

> She likes one when she gets home from work.

The sentence can be reworked to include that piece of information.

> Mum likes a cup of tea when she gets home from work.
> When she gets home from work mum likes a cup of tea.
> Mum, when she gets home from work, likes a cup of tea.

❑ Try putting the extra information below into each of the sentences.

sentences	extra information
Mum hires a car.	She hires it when we go on holidays.
Our teacher wore a suit today.	He is usually scruffy.
The children had to walk.	They had missed the bus.
Our computer went to the repair shop.	It has stopped working.
Sam went to the hospital.	This was after he fell off the slide.
Grandad washed his hands.	This was before he made a cake.
Everyone cheered Sara.	She had scored a goal.

reworked sentences

1. _____

2. _____

3. _____

4. _____

5. _____

6. _____

7. _____

Constructing complex

❑ Look at this extract from Ted Hughes's *The Iron Man*.
Using coloured pencils underline the different clauses in different colours.
Circle any words or punctuation marks used to separate or join the clauses.

At last he stopped, and looked at the sea. Was he thinking the sea had stolen his ear? Perhaps he was thinking the sea had come up, while he lay scattered, and had gone down again with his ear.

He walked towards the sea. He walked into the breakers, and there he stood for a while, the breakers bursting around his knees. Then he walked in deeper, deeper, deeper.

The gulls took off and glided down low over the great iron head that was now moving slowly out through the swell. The eyes blazed red, level with the wavetops, till a big wave covered them and foam spouted over the top of the head. The head still moved out under water. The eyes and the top of the head appeared for a moment in a hollow of the swell. Now the eyes were green. then the sea covered them and the head.

The gulls circled low over the line of bubbles that went on moving slowly out into the deep sea.

PHOTOCOPIABLE

Connecting and altering sentences

Contents of Term 1b

Unit 1: **Connectives**	Investigate connecting words and phrases
Unit 2: **Collecting connectives**	Classify different connecting words and phrases
Unit 3: **Framing connectives**	Investigate connectives in different kinds of text
Unit 4: **Active and passive**	Work with sentences in the active and passive voice
Unit 5: **Developing punctuation**	Secure knowledge of colon, semicolon, parenthetic commas, dashes and brackets

---

This half-term

Connecting words and phrases provide children with a vital resource with which they can structure a varied range of sentences. This set of units provides an opportunity for children to investigate a range of connectives. It also provides an introduction to the active and passive forms of sentences.

Poster notes

Type of connection
This poster provides an outline of the various types of connection looked in this half-term. The list of connectives could include a significant number of further examples but the main focus should be upon the function these words perform. Once children can see this they can classify such words and phrases for themselves.

Parentheses
The use of parentheses is introduced in this poster, showing the main ways in which additional information can be slotted into the middle of a sentence.

Types of connection

Type of connectives	Connectives that add one thing to another	Connectives that oppose things
Examples	and also	but however

Type of connectives	Connectives showing something caused something else	Connectives that place things in time
Examples	because so therefore	then and then after

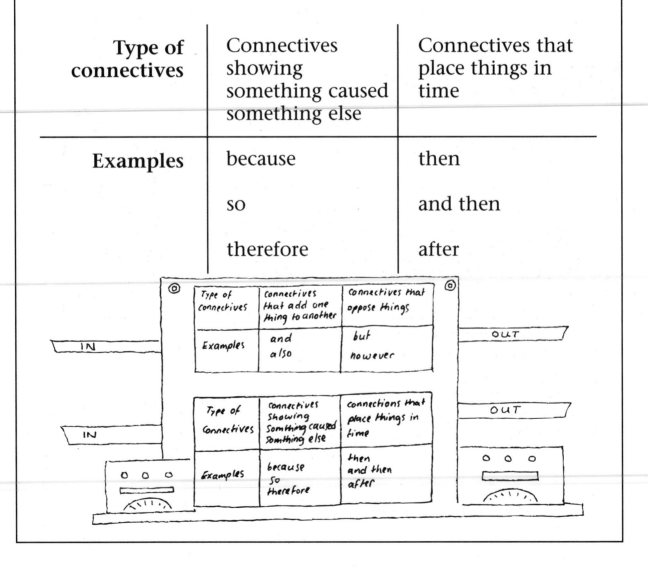

Parentheses

Explanatory words and phases are called parentheses.
These can be inserted into sentences using parenthetic
brackets, commas or dashes. For example, the sentence:
Mr Brown shouted.

This can take the addition of an
explanatory parenthesis in three
ways, for example:
Mr Brown (the caretaker) shouted.
Mr Brown, the caretaker, shouted.
Mr Brown - the caretaker - shouted.

Connectives

Objective
Investigate connecting words and phrases

Language issues
Clauses are units of language that include at least a subject and a verb. They can be parts of sentences or whole sentences. The space between clauses can be marked by connecting words. Words like 'and', 'but' and 'because' link clauses together.

For example: I went to school and I regretted it.

or   I went to school but I got out at home time.

Words that connect two clauses can appear at the beginning of a sentence as in the above examples. They can also come at the start of a sentence. In the sentence 'Because I've got homework I can't go out' the connective is 'because'. It connects the two clauses 'I can't go out' and 'I've got homework'.

Ways of teaching
Many teachers have experienced the task of trying to break children's dependence upon the word 'and'. The stories that run 'I went to the park and I played on the swing and I went to the shop and I saw my friend and I...' are badly in need of some variation in the language used to connect clauses and sentences.

About the activities
Photocopiable: Connective starters
The idea of connective words at the start of a sentence is a difficult one to handle. Through experimenting with completing these sentence children can investigate the way such words work.

Photocopiable: Connected sentences
Following the 'Connective starters' activity children can revisit these sentences by producing examples of their own.

Photocopiable: Using connectives
This activity also asks children to use various connectives, this time in the middle of sentences. As the activity progresses the challenge is to construct a lengthy sentence with more than one connective suggested.

Following up
Starter finding: Children can look in a range of texts for sentences that begin with a connecting word or phrase. They can make a note of the connection and the clauses it connects.

Starter and finisher: Working in two teams children can take turns to devise a sentence that starts with a connective and a first clause, like the incomplete sentences in 'Connective starters'. Team A produces one of these that team B has to complete. Alternatively you can ask team B to produce three ways of ending the sentence.

The longest!: Using the various connective words shown in this unit children can try producing the longest sentence with the greatest number of connectives. for example. 'Without thinking about what we were writing we produced this long sentence because our teacher set us the challenge but made out we wouldn't be able to do it so we couldn't resist however....' To make it more challenging you can specify that each connective can only be used once.

Connective starters

Words that connect two clauses often appear in the middle of a sentence:
I can't go out **because** I've got homework.

They can also appear at the start of a sentence.
Because I've got homework I can't go out.

In this sentence 'Because' connects
Because I've got homework I can't go out.

❏ Look at these sentences. The connecting word is at the beginning. It is followed by the first clause. Can you complete the sentence?

Since I started school _____

As you like drawing so much _____

Because of my teacher _____

After I finish my lunch _____

Whenever I go out to play _____

Although I am at school _____

While waiting for a bus _____

Until it is time to go home _____

Connected sentences

❏ Try creating sentences with connecting words at the beginning.

Since	
As	
Because	
After	
Whenever	
Although	
While	
Until	

Using connectives

❑ Try using the connectives in a sentence.
For example:

| but | I wanted to play out but it was time for tea. |

| and/but | I wanted to go outside and I asked my mum but she said it was time for tea. |

| and | |

| therefore | |

| and/but | |

| and/because | |

| but/because | |

| and/then | |

| then/but | |

| and/then/but | |

Collecting connectives

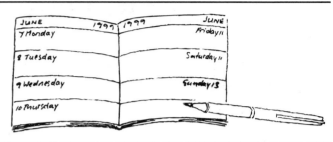

Objective
Classify different connecting words and phrases

Language issues
There are four ways in which clauses can be connected. These are shown in the table below:

Type of connection	Addition	Opposition	Cause	Time
Function	words to add things	words to oppose things	things causing other things	the times when things happened
Examples	and also	but however	because so therefore	then and then after

Ways of teaching
Through looking at the purpose of connectives children can begin to see the varied words they could use to perform these functions.

About the activities
Photocopiable: Connective collection
As an initial stimulus to looking at the variety of connectives, this activity asks children to list some varied examples found in different texts. If the texts they are using are disposable they could cut out the various examples and add them to a class collection.

Photocopiable: Connection jobs
The sentences in this activity provide examples of a variety of connective functions, matching the four functions on the poster and presented in 'Language Issues'.

Photocopiable: Dear Diary
As children read the lively diary entry they can circle the various connective words. They could try circling words doing different jobs in different colours. They could also try to figure out what each connecting word or phrase is connecting together.

Following up
Diary extract: Children can try using a range of connective words in their own diary extract, modelled upon the example in 'Dear Diary'. As they look at the various words they could use to connect clause to clause, they should examine the different functions the words are performing.

Colour coding: Looking at a range of texts, children can circle different connecting words and phrases in different colours depending upon the job they are doing. Looking at the four functions connectives can perform, children can ascribe a colour to each job and seek out their examples.

Thesaurus: Using a Thesaurus children can search out alternative connectives to the ones they have found in various texts.

Connective collection

❏ Collect a variety of texts together –
for example, newspapers, leaflets, packaging,
recipe book, games instructions...

❏ Find the connecting words used in these texts.

Text	Connecting words and phrases
"Safe Crossing" road safety poster	first then before but and

Connection jobs

Connecting words and phrases can do different jobs.
Some connecting words add one thing to another.

| I like chips and I like them from the chip shop. |

Some connecting words oppose things.

| I was hungry so I bought some chips. |

| I ate some chips because I was hungry. |

Some connecting words show that something caused something else.

| I like chips but I can't afford them. |

Some connecting words place things in time

| I had some chips then I went and had some more. |

❑ Try sorting the connecting words in these sentences into the four types.

Addition Connectives: that add one thing to another

Cause Connectives: showing something caused something else

Opposition Connectives: that oppose things

Time Connectives: that place things in time

We were very shocked on finding that Granny is a secret agent.

Besides being a brilliant doctor my sister happens to be a first-class ice skater!

One of my brothers is a pop star whereas the other is a doctor.

We sat down to eat our tea as Grandad tamed a lion.

Before she goes to bed my little sister flies around the room.

Either Dad turns into a werewolf or he stands in the street and moos.

Dear Diary

❑ Look at this diary entry and find the connecting words and phrases. What sort of job are they doing? What clauses are they connecting?

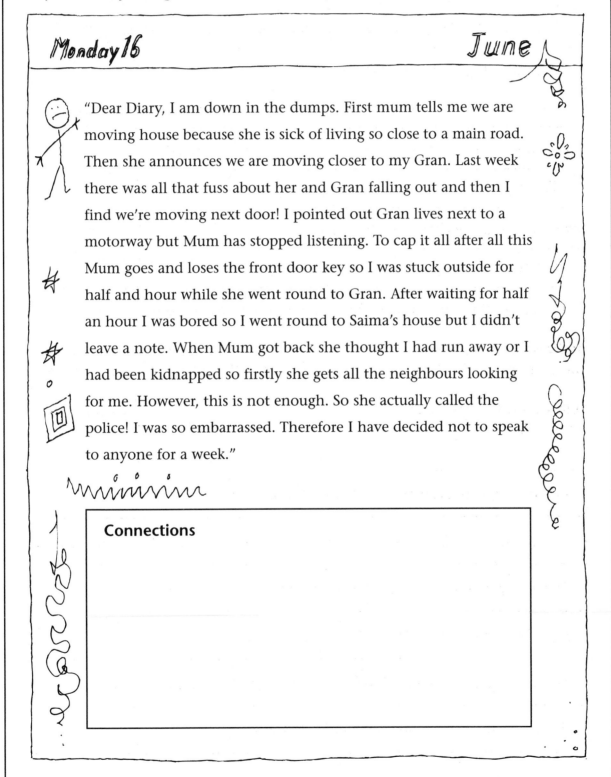

Monday 16   **June**

"Dear Diary, I am down in the dumps. First mum tells me we are moving house because she is sick of living so close to a main road. Then she announces we are moving closer to my Gran. Last week there was all that fuss about her and Gran falling out and then I find we're moving next door! I pointed out Gran lives next to a motorway but Mum has stopped listening. To cap it all after all this Mum goes and loses the front door key so I was stuck outside for half and hour while she went round to Gran. After waiting for half an hour I was bored so I went round to Saima's house but I didn't leave a note. When Mum got back she thought I had run away or I had been kidnapped so firstly she gets all the neighbours looking for me. However, this is not enough. So she actually called the police! I was so embarrassed. Therefore I have decided not to speak to anyone for a week."

Connections

Framing connectives

Objective
Investigate connectives in different kinds of text

Language issues
Various types of text use certain grammatical styles. Instructions are written as imperatives, for example:
'Boil the egg for...'
Diaries, however, are written in the form of recounted events, for example:
'I boiled the egg for...'.
Explanatory texts such as science texts usually use simple present tenses:
'When an egg is boiled it...'
The features of each provide a frame, a set of conventions in which various text types are structured.

Ways of teaching
As children develop the scope of their writing they need to use different words and phrases to structure their compositions. A child who is writing a report of a science experiment or an argument against factory farming needs to think of the appropriate way of framing their text otherwise they will usually resort to producing a narrative. Recent research has shown the value of writing frames as a means of helping children to structure their writing. Frames provide the opening phrases of particular sections in a piece of writing.

About the activities
Photocopiable: Different types of text.
By looking at different types of text children can find various connectives in use. The linking of the language and purpose of the texts is a complex activity and may require some support.

Photocopiable: Toys and tricks
The two texts shown provide an opportunity for children to pick out some of the different types of connective. They could discuss the way in which this is a feature of the types of text used.

Photocopiable: Text language
This activity does not purport to teach instructional or persuasive writing. Building upon the skills of producing different types of writing that children will develop elsewhere, this activity provides an opportunity to extend work done with the photocopiable 'Toys and tricks' , looking at the language children will use to produce different types of text.

Following up
Magazine examples: Within one magazine children can find a range of different types of text. They can look for the connecting words and phrases within them. A news story will differ from a recipe and they will both differ from a weather report or an explanation of how something works. By focusing upon a single magazine children can narrow the search but still trawl through a wide range of examples.

Persuade and instruct: Children can try to produce a variety of persuasive and instructive texts. For a fuller account of the use of frames to support writing, as well as some practical guidance, teachers should look at *Developing Children's Non Fiction Writing: working with writing frames* by Maureen Lewis and David Wray (Scholastic).

Toys and tricks

❏ Look at these two texts from a magazine. They are doing different jobs. One is persuading. The other is giving instructions.
Look at the different connecting words and phrases used.

SOAPBOX

My name is Sean Prentice and I am at Severton Comprehensive School, Nottingham.

I propose that children's toys should not be advertised on television because the adverts just make children want more toys. The toys are shown doing fantastic things with the result that children really want them. This is made even worse because the adverts can make toys look bright and fast. The toys are often very expensive so children cannot afford them and therefore they nag their parents. Manufacturers say their adverts just present information. This means that banning them would be unfair on children. However, I think children see enough advertising in toy shops and comics and so they don't need the amount they see on television.

TRICK OF THE WEEK

To do this mindreading trick you will need an audience and a partner who has already discussed the trick with you. First you and your partner must agree a signal, such as scratching your head or putting a hand in your pocket. This will be your 'cue'. Then you try the trick out on your audience.

Begin by asking your partner to leave the room.
Once this is done ask the audience to pick an object in the room.
After they have chosen an object ask your partner back into the room.

When your partner returns explain that you will communicate which object the audience chose by mind power. Go round various objects asking 'Is it this?' Your partner should say 'No'. When you reach the one the audience chose do the secret sign. Then your partner knows this is the chosen object and will astound your audience by answering 'Yes'. Amazing!

Different types of text

❑ Look at the connecting words and phrases in different texts.
What links are there between the connectives used and the job they do?

Text: Diary extract		
Connecting words and phrases	**What job does the text do?**	**Links between connections and job**
and, then, after that, while	Tells about things that happened during a day.	The connections sort out the time things happened.

You could look at how things that happen are explained in a science book, how instructions are given in a notice on the wall or how events are sorted in a history book.

Text:		
Connecting words and phrases	**What job does the text do?**	**Links between connections and job**

Text:		

Text:		

Text language

❏ Look at the texts in 'Toys and tricks'. Try writing your own persuasive argument and your own procedural instructions. Produce two short examples. You can use some of the words and phrases suggested below to help you.

A text to persuade

Suggested words and phrases:
I propose
say
because
with the result that
so
therefore
and so

A text to instruct

Suggested words and phrases:
To
you will need
first
then
begin by
once this is done
after
when

A text to persuade:

A text to instruct:

Active and passive

Objective
Work with sentences in the active and passive voice

Language issues
The Language issue introduced within this unit is 'voice'. (It is covered more fully in the Language Issues and activities found in Term 2a.)

An action like 'The dog chased the cat' is written in the active voice. The dog is the subject of the sentence and is doing the action denoted by the verb.

The same action could be described in the following way: 'The cat was chased by the dog'.

In this case the cat is the subject of the sentence. However, the cat isn't actively doing the action denoted by the verb. Instead the cat is the 'passive' subject, to whom the verb is done. The following examples show the same contrast between sentences about active doers of the verb and passive subjects to whom the verb is done.

The cook scrambled the eggs.

The eggs were scrambled by the cook.

The artist painted the picture.

The picture was painted by the artist.

Ways of teaching
This is an introduction to the idea of active and passive voice. While there are technical ways of explaining the idea of active and passive (the passive voice takes the verb 'to be') this is one of those areas teachers often present to their children with a slightly unsound but workable distinction. This is that active sentences are where someone 'does' and passive are where they are 'done to'. Obviously the distinction is simplistic but as working guidance it tends to provide the necessary idea.

About the activities
Photocopiable: Fill the sentence
The missing sections from the sentences on this photocopiable could be in the active or passive voice. Children don't need to be familiar with the concept of active and passive voice for this. They just need to look for the 'sentence middle' that makes sense. However, as they undertake the activity the teacher can discuss how they made their selection and compare the effect of using the two types of verb.

Photocopiable: Doing or done?
As with the previous photocopiable this activity looks at active and passive voice without introducing children to the specific terms. The distinction they have to make in this activity concerns the person who is the subject of each sentence. They need to ask whether the person is actively doing the action in the sentence (for example. 'Sam soaked Lou') or having something done to them (for example. 'Sam was soaked by Lou'). The activity provides a way of introducing the words 'active' and 'passive' by asking questions like 'Is Sam actively soaking Lou?' and 'Is Sam passively being soaked?').

Photocopiable: 'Was' and 'by' sentences
The 'was' and 'by' examples and model sentences provide a way for children to attempt to produce their own examples of passive sentences. They will need to identify a verb that can fit in the middle space and participants either side. Asking them to begin with some interesting verbs, or giving possible verbs they could use, provides a way of getting the activity started.

Following up
Examples in texts: Children can look through various texts to find examples of verbs done by a someone or done to someone. They could look at which is most common in different types of text and discuss the effect upon meaning that using the passive voice has.

Fill the sentence

❑ Look at the sentences below. Each of them has a piece missing from the middle. Cut out the sentences and find the missing word or words in the 'sentence middles' box. Stick the complete sentence onto a sheet of paper with the correct sentence middle.

sentence middles

was chased by	chased	painted	was melted by	scrambled
was painted by	melted	put out	was put out by	were scrambled by

The dog	the cat.
The cook	the eggs.
The artist	the picture.
The cat	the dog.
The sun	the snow.
The eggs	the cook.
The fire	the fire-fighters.
The picture	the artist.
The fire-fighters	the fire.
The snow	the sun.

Doing or done?

The subject of each of the sentences below is in bold.
Is the subject doing something? Or is something being done to the subject?

Callum helped Josh with his picture.	**Josh** was helped by Callum.
Lisa gave Danny his present.	**Danny** was given a present by Lisa.
Lisa was given a present by Danny.	**Danny** gave Lisa a present.
The princess saved the prince.	**The prince** was saved by the princess.
Sam soaked Lou with the hose.	**Sam** was soaked by Lou throwing water.
The burglar ran from the police.	**The burglar** was scared by the police car.
Jack was tripped up by Jill.	**Jill** tripped Jack up.
The policewoman chased the burglar.	**The burglar** was chased by the police.
Chloe lost her little sister in the supermarket.	**Chloe's** sister was left in the supermarket.
On Tuesday, **my uncle** went shopping.	**I** was bought a present by my uncle.

❑ Cut out the sentences and sort them into two groups:
• ones in which the person in bold is doing something
• and ones in which something is 'done to' the person in bold by someone or something.

'Was' and 'by' sentences

❑ Look at these sentences. In each of them **something was done by someone or something.**

Chloe	was	scared	by	the frightening mask.
The farmer	was	chased	by	the bull.
The earth	was	saved	by	Superwoman.

❑ Try making your own 'was' and 'by' sentences in the spaces below.

_____ was _____ by _____

_____ was _____ by _____

_____ was _____ by _____

_____ was _____ by _____

_____ was _____ by _____

_____ was _____ by _____

_____ was _____ by _____

_____ was _____ by _____

Developing punctuation

Objective
Secure knowledge of colon, semicolon, parenthetic commas, dashes and brackets

Language issues
Colons are used to introduce lists. For example:
'For this experiment you will need: a glass of water, a teaspoon of salt.'
or summaries:
'We have learned the following: salt dissolves in water...'
or examples:
'Some materials dissolve, for example: salt in water, sugar in coffee.'
or quotations.
'My teacher always says: "The colon is a funny little mark".'

Colons introduce second clauses that expand or illustrate the first:
'The water evaporated: it turned into water vapour.'
It separates one clause from another, without cutting the two off like a full stop.

Semicolons can separate two closely linked clauses:
'The water evaporated; I said it would.'
They show there is some link between the two things separated:
'Salt dissolves in water; sugar does too.'
They can be used to separate complicated items in a list (where a comma won't do the job so well):
'Our saucers contained salt, water and sugar; salt and water; sugar and water; water on its own.'

Semicolons are stronger than commas but weaker than full stops.

Explanatory words and phases are called parentheses. These can be inserted into sentences using parenthetic brackets , commas or dashes. For example, the sentence 'Mr Brown shouted.' can take the addition of an explanatory parenthesis in three different ways:
Mr Brown (the caretaker) shouted.
Mr Brown, the caretaker, shouted.
Mr Brown – the caretaker – shouted.

Ways of teaching
Colons and semicolons are difficult pieces of punctuation to place. The specific jobs that each can perform merge into unclear territory in some sentences that could take a semicolon or a comma. To some extent part of learning these punctuation marks involves training children to use their judgement.

About the activities
Photocopiable: Placing colons and semicolons
As a way of revising colons and semicolons this activity asks children to place them within sentences. They could try the activity and compare their results with a partner, justifying their choice for the placing of the punctuation. Review the uses of colons and semicolons with children before setting this activity.

The suggested answers to the sentences on this photocopiable are as follows (including capitalization):
Gran thinks I am scruffy; Mum agrees.
The kettle boiled; I thought it would.
The dog stopped running; the cat did as well.
Nobody found the lost key; that spelled trouble.
Sam thought he needed trainers; Mum didn't.
The detective caught the thief; just as I thought.
Someone left the taps on; that was silly.
The three packets of crisps were: salt and vinegar, cheese and onion and ready salted.
When she switches the light off Mum always says: "get to sleep or else!"
Our class has resolved the following: we will tidy up quicker and line up quieter.

Photocopiable: Possible parenthesis
Through investigating the possibilities for extra information presented by a sentence, children can develop their understanding of where and why parenthetic phrases are inserted in sentences.

Photocopiable: Parenthetic words
This activity gives children practice with the three different ways of demarcating parentheses. They can draw upon notes made in the 'Possible parentheses' activity to provide examples of the different ways they can demarcate the pieces of extra information.

Following up
Children can examine articles from newspapers and magazines and collect examples of each type of punctuation, noting the effect that each has upon meaning.

Placing colons and semicolons

❑ These sentences have had their punctuation removed. Rewrite these sentences placing punctuation marks in the correct place. Each sentence could include a colon or semicolon.

gran thinks I am scruffy mum agrees

the three packets of crisps were salt and vinegar cheese
and onion ready salted

nobody found the lost key that spelt trouble

the kettle boiled I thought it would

our class has resolved the following we will tidy up quicker and
line up quieter

the detective caught the thief just as I thought

the dog stopped running the cat did as well

when she switches the light off mum always says get to sleep or else

sam thought he needed new trainers mum didnt

someone left the taps on that was silly

Possible parenthesis

❑ Look at this sentence: **Mr Brown found the key in the desk.**

There are all sorts of bits of explanation that could be added.

Mr Brown found the key in the desk. _____ where he kept his teeth, where
all the other keys are kept

our teacher, the local   which he had lost, which had
vet, whoever he is!   been lost for a hundred years

❑ Try inventing bits of explanation that could be
added to these sentences.

❑ Make up the information – as wild as you want.

Corky put the map in the chest.

The burglar left the sack in the trolley.

Marie threw the box out of the window.

Josh made the potion in the cellar.

The secret sign was drawn by Ms. Coles.

Sara caught the thief in a trap.

Parenthetic words

Parenthetic words are inserted into a sentence to explain something. Look at this example from 'Possible parenthesis':

Mr Brown found the key in the desk.

our teacher

Information like this could be inserted into a sentence and marked off by:

brackets   Mr Brown (our teacher) found the key in the desk.

or commas   Mr Brown, our teacher, found the key in the desk.

or dashes   Mr Brown – our teacher – found the key in the desk.

❏ Create three sentences using a parenthesis marked by the three methods.

❏ You could use sentences and notes made on the 'Possible parenthesis' page.

use brackets	
use commas	
use dashes	
use brackets	
use commas	
use dashes	
use brackets	
use commas	
use dashes	

Formal language

Contents of Term 2a

This half-term

In this unit children engage in a thorough investigation of the active and passive voice. This is a complex idea but builds upon ideas about clauses and verbs with which children will be familiar. As part of this set of units children begin to look at the formalities that can affect the use of language.

Poster notes

Active and passive
This poster provides a fairly detailed presentation of the way in which active voiced clauses can be transformed into passives. The process can be shared in a whole-class read of the poster but should be followed with children's attempts to make that change for themselves.

Active and passive sentences
The various sentences on this poster contain verbs in the active and passive voice. No pointers are given to which is which. Children can try to identify the different types of verb voice for themselves. They can also try to change sentences written in one voice into another. Note that in some the agent is hidden (see Unit 3).

Active and passive

Actions can be written in the **active voice** or the **passive voice**.

In the active voice the action is done by a subject:
The lion chased the zebra.
Subject   Verb

In the passive voice the action is done to a subject:
The lion was chased by the zebra.
            Verb   Subject

Sentences can be changed from the active voice to the passive voice.

Gran broke the plate.   **The plate was broken by Gran.**

This usually involves the subject (who does the
verb) moving to after the verb (and becoming the
agent):

Gran
broke ▾

plate
▾ broke

and the object (to whom the verb was done) moving
to before the verb (and becoming the subject):

The verb has a word like 'was' or 'were' added and the word 'by'
to show who did the action

The plate *was* **broken** *by* **Gran.**

For example
The plate was broken by Gran.

Active and passive sentences

The dog chased the children.

The children were chased by the dog.

The boy found the keys.

The keys were found by the boy.

Sam made this cake.

This cake was made by Sam.

Active and passive

Objective
Secure the use of the terms active and passive

Language issues
Sentences usually contain at least one verb. The subject of a sentence is the person or thing involved in that action. In a simple sentence like 'Jack laughed' the subject is 'Jack' and the verb is 'laughed'.

At their very minimum clauses are made up of a subject and verb. They can also include an object. This is the person or thing to whom the verb is done – for example:

Jack	found	his keys.
subject	*verb*	*object*
Chloe	built	a house.
subject	*verb*	*object*
Molly	caught	the burglar.
subject	*verb*	*object*

Each of the above is written in the active voice, with the subject actively doing the verb.

Alternatively the subject can be the one to whom the verb was done. Such sentences are written in the passive voice and the doer of the verb is referred to as the agent, for example:

The keys	were found by	Jack.
subject	*verb*	*agent*
This house	was built by	Chloe.
subject	*verb*	*agent*
A burglar	was caught by	Molly.
subject	*verb*	*agent*

Ways of teaching
In this unit children are very much 'steered' towards an understanding of the passive. They are asked to complete sentences that can only be finished if they use the passive voice. This should give them an opportunity to exercise a way of phrasing sentences they will have encountered in reading but will be less experienced at writing.

About the activities
Photocopiable: Sentence flipping
Reading the active and completing the passive sentences in this activity will involve the children in trying out the phrasing involved in writing passive sentences. At Year 6 they will have encountered the passive in reading but it is still comparatively rare in their writing. One point to emphasize as they remodel the sentences: they should try to include all the information from the active sentence in their passive version. If the sentence reads:

'The fierce, little dog chased the children' they need to include all the adjectives in their passive version ('The children were chased by the fierce, little dog.'), rather than just writing: 'The children were chased by the dog'.

Photocopiable: Active or passive
This sorting activity focuses upon the basic idea of active and passive voice, asking them to distinguish between the use of these two styles in a range of sentences. There is a similarity between a number of the examples but children have to look for the basic active/passive distinction.

Photocopiable: 'Cut and paste' passives
This activity involves children in physically cutting up sentences to change their voice. They may realize that they do not need to cut out each individual word. If so, they can just cut the sentences where necessary.

Following up
Text shading: Children can read a newspaper article shading active clauses in red and passives in blue. They can look at which is more common and see if this is a feature of one article or of the paper as a whole.

Sentence cutting: Children can try to produce their own 'Cut and paste' passives using sentences cut out of leaflets and magazines. They may need to write over capital letters that were originally at the start of a sentence and that now appear in the middle.

Sentence flipping

This sentence │ The dog chased the cat. │ can be flipped over so that the end

comes at the beginning: │ The cat was chased by the dog. │

❑ Try doing the same with these sentences.
Finish the 'flipped' sentences:

The cat chased the mouse.	The mouse was
My mum made this cake.	This cake
I found the keys.	The keys
We painted the large picture.	The large picture
Sam, Jake and Chloe tidied Gran's garden.	Gran's garden was
Shona wrote the scary story.	The scary story
The fierce, little dog chased the children.	The children
All the teachers in our school wrote our school play.	Our school play was written
The shopkeeper and his children painted the front of the shop.	The front of the shop
Carlos glued and painted the model.	The model

PHOTOCOPIABLE

Active or passive

Actions can be written in the **active voice** or the **passive voice**.

In the active voice the action is done by a subject:

The lion   chased   the zebra.
Subject   *Verb*   *agent*

In the passive voice the action is done to a subject:

The zebra   was chased by   the lion.
Subject   *Verb*   *agent*

The agent is whoever or whatever made the verb happen.

❑ Cut out the rectangles and sort the sentences into **active voice** and **passive voice**.

✂

The monster chased the goblin.	The window was broken by the football.
The goblin was chased by the monster.	Laura scored a goal.
Sam found the lost key.	The key was found by Sam.
The monster was chased by the goblin.	On Tuesday Mum went to town.
Sam lost the key.	The goblin chased the monster.
The boy made the sandwich.	The children performed the play.
The key was lost by Sam.	The sandwich was made by the boy.
A goal was scored by Laura.	The parents were entertained by the play.

'Cut and paste' passives

❑ Look at these sentences. They are all active sentences. The subject does the action.

At	the	park	a	goose	chased	my	brother.

Today	our	caretaker	repaired	the	computer.

At	playtime	my	friend	invented	a	game.

In	assembly	our	teacher	played	the	piano.

In	the	garden	a	wasp	stung	my	Gran.

After	school	my	Aunty	mended	my	bike.

Last	summer	my	uncle	built	our	treehouse.

After	dinner	the	children	cleared	the	table.

❑ Change the sentences by cutting them up

In	the	garden	a	wasp	stung	my	Gran.

and adding the words 'was' and 'by' from the collection below.
Put them either side of the verb.

In	the	garden	a	wasp	was	stung	by	my	Gran.

You will need to swap the nouns around for it to make sense.

In	the	garden	my	Gran	was	stung	by	a	wasp.

❑ Stick the new sentences onto a sheet of paper.

was	by
was	by
was	by
was	by
was	by
was	by

Active and passive changes

Objective
Know how active and passive can be reordered

Language issues
Sentences can be altered from the active to the passive voice.

Jack   found   his keys.
subject   verb   object

The simplest way of understanding this process is by looking at how the verb changes. From the straightforward 'found' the passive form typically involves:

❑ the addition of the word 'by' after the verb – for example:
'chased by'
'built by'

❑ a form of the verb 'be', such as 'was', 'is' or 'are' before the verb (or a form of the verb 'get'):
'were found by'
'is helped by'
'got replaced by'.

The other alteration takes place around the verb as the object of the active form of the verb becomes the subject of a passive. So Jack's keys, the object in the above example, become the subject of the passive verb:

The keys   were found by   Jack.
subject   verb   agent

Ways of teaching
The focus of this unit is a relatively straightforward concentration upon how sentences in one voice can be rewritten in another. Once again the way words like 'was' or 'is' and 'by' stand alongside a passive verb can provide a way of getting children to think about how active verbs can be remodelled. Faced with a sentence like 'Chester hates school' they need to imagine these words around that verb. Once they can visualize that they start to realize how the verb needs to change and how the sentence can change around to include the verbal form 'is hated by'.

About the activities
Photocopiable: Transforming sentences
The emphasis in this activity is upon children making sentences passive. This involves the process outlined on the page. In doing this they need to focus upon the verb. Once the basic change is made to the verb the other words fit in around it.

Photocopiable: Changing voices
To undertake this activity children will need access to a range of texts. The teacher may want to provide some leeway for children to simplify sentences in the active voice, picking out a particular clause from within a complex example. The main point of the activity is to get the children looking at how sentences and clauses in a real context can be altered.

Photocopiable: Sentence switching
As children look at the table they should develop their ability at switching sentences from one voice to another. As they do this they can also look at the sorts of changes they are having to make to various pieces of language to shape the transformation.

Following up
The reading scheme: Looking at some of the reading books within school children can try to alter the voice of the verbs throughout these texts. Reading schemes will provide a lot of examples of the active voice that children can switch to the passive voice.

Passive back: One of the most effective ways of achieving a whole-class concentration on the remodelling of sentences is to try 'passive back'. The teacher says a sentence in the active voice and children have to say it back in the passive. This can provide a lot of shouting and sharing across the group as they contribute to the attempt to say a passive. The passive is not common in speech so there are often lively exchanges.

Transforming sentences

Sentences can be changed from the active voice to the passive voice.

| Gran broke the plate. | The plate was broken by Gran. |

This usually involves
the subject (who does the verb) moving to after the verb.

Gran
broke

and the object (to whom the verb was done) moving to
before the verb.

plate
broke

The verb has a word like 'was' or 'were' added and the word 'by' to show who
did the action

The plate ^{was} broken ^{by} Gran.

These sentences are written in an active voice.
Can you change them to a passive voice?

The cat chased the bird.	
Our teacher painted a picture.	
Saima found my dinner money.	
The wind blew the tree.	
The sun evaporated the puddle.	
Mum repaired the car.	
The cow ate the grass.	
A bus knocked down the lamppost.	
The thief stole the chocolate.	
The teachers sang a song.	

Changing voices

❑ Look through various texts, such as magazines, newspapers, story books or textbooks.

❑ Using this table find some sentences written in the active voice. Can you rewrite them in a passive voice?

Sentence in active voice	Rewritten in passive voice

Sentence switching

❏ Look at the clauses in the table below.
Where the clause is in the active voice, write it in the passive voice.

Active voice	Passive voice
I hid the key	The key was hidden by me

Where the clause is in the passive voice write it in the active voice.

Active voice	Passive voice
I hid the key	The key was hidden by me

Active voice	Passive voice
The pirates drew the map.	
	The treasure was buried by pirates.
	The map was stolen by a thief.
The thief lost the map.	
We found the map.	
	The map was followed by us.
We found the treasure.	
The museum looked after the treasure.	

The agent

Objective

Consider how the passive voice can conceal the agent of a sentence

Language issues

In the passive form of the verb the agent can be removed and the sentence will still make sense. The passive:

The keys	were found by	Jack.
subject	*verb*	*agent*
This house	was built by	Chloe.
subject	*verb*	*agent*

can have the agent removed, along with the word 'by'.

The keys	were found.
subject	*verb*
This house	was built.
subject	*verb*

Agent-less sentences like this are common in certain types of non-fiction texts, such as the write-up of a science experiment:

'The solution was heated. At boiling point the solution was poured into the crystals. The crystals were frozen etc...' No mention here of who did the heating and pouring – the presence of the agent is implicit. Removing the agent can be seen as creating a more distant type of writing, suited to legal and factual texts.

Ways of teaching

This unit introduces children to a way of phrasing things with which they will be quite unfamiliar. The emphasis is upon them looking at the way a sentence can show or conceal the agent and one of the most effective ways that this will be achieved is if they start to notice examples of their own (see 'Hidden agents' in the Following up activities).

About the activities

Photocopiable: Sentence questions

The sentences in this exercise have all had the agent removed. Children can look at these and raise questions about who the agent could be. The sentences are all altered versions of passive sentences used in the previous two units, which should help children to figure out who the missing person is.

Photocopiable: Hide the agent

By remodelling the sentences shown, children can try to hide the agent in passive verbs. One useful point for them to look out for is the word 'by'. This is the point at which the agent is described. The final two sentences are

more difficult as the agent appears in the middle and can be cut while leaving a piece at the end: 'The fridge was defrosted because it was full of ice.' 'School was painted so now it looks better.'

Photocopiable: Passive diary challenge

The passive diary challenge involves children in an extreme use of the passive voice. It is not the natural mode of diary writing so the exercise leads to oddities of language and presents quite a challenge.

Following up

Odd texts: As with the passive diary children could try to write other texts that would normally be actively voiced in the passive. They could try a letter to a friend or an explanation of how a problem occurred on the playground.

Excuses: One place to look out for the passive voice with the agent removed is when the agent is being hidden. To announce: 'The vase has been broken' begs the question 'Who broke it?'. Children could try to write their own list of agentless admissions to things they could have done, such as 'The cake has been eaten', and 'Water has been spilled all over the kitchen floor'.

Hidden agents: Children can look for hidden agents in other texts. Factual textbooks can be interesting places to look for sentences like the ones shown in 'Language issues'.

Sentence questions

❑ Look at this sentence.

| **The cakes were made.** |

It doesn't say who 'made the cakes'.
The agent has been removed.

| **The agent is whoever or whatever** made the cakes. |

It could have said 'The cakes were made by the cook.'

❑ Look at these sentences and try to describe the missing agent.

The agent is whoever or whatever.

The grass was eaten.	
The keys were found.	
My Gran was stung.	
A bird was chased.	
The car was repaired.	
A song was sung.	
My dinner money was found.	
The chocolate was stolen.	
The goblin was chased.	
The picture was painted.	

Hide the agent

Passive sentences can be written in a way that shows the agent.

The lion was chased by the zebra.
Subject   Verb   agent

> Now everyone knows it was me.

You can remove the agent and they still make sense.

The zebra was chased.
Subject   Verb

❏ Try rewriting these sentences with the agent removed.

The lion was chased by a vicious mouse.	
My mum was scared by the horror film.	
Sam and Jodie were invited to tea by the woman who lived in the cottage.	
The world was saved by Superwoman and her superdog.	
At the cafe, tea was made by the people in the kitchen.	
Before we started our play the curtain was raised by Sharlee and Kieron.	
When the train stopped the doors were opened by the driver.	
At the end of school the bell was rung by our secretary.	
The fridge was defrosted by the caretaker because it was full of ice.	
School was painted by the decorators so now it looks better.	

Passive diary challenge

When we write a diary we say what we did:

It is a challenge to try writing one in the passive voice.

Dear diary
Today I made my breakfast and caught the bus to school. I played football. We did our maths then we watched a television programme...

Dear diary
My breakfast was made by me and the bus was caught to school. Football was played and maths was done. A television programme was watched...

❏ Try writing a diary entry about your day. Write it in the passive voice. Try to remove the agent!

Dear diary

Formal language

Objective
Understand features of formal language, collecting and analysing examples

Language issues
Formal or official documents have certain characteristics that distinguish them from the friendly note or informal narrative. They commonly use impersonal subjects, such as 'the vendor' or 'the proprietor', to refer to people. They also contain terminology of their own: words and phrases like 'In the eventuality...' or 'Herewith....' instead of plain 'Should...' and 'From now on...'. The extreme example is the use of Latin phrases in certain legal documents. The obscure language of such documentation has even led to the setting up of a Plain English Campaign to tackle the obscure nature of the language of officialdom!

In linguistics the term 'register' refers to the social conditioning of a piece of language. The wedding service that begins with the formal 'Dearly beloved, we are gathered here together...' does so because it is set in a legal and ritual context in which the opening 'Hey – we're here' would be too informal. The social context determines the type of language used.

Ways of teaching
The teacher should try to steer away from the idea that formal language is 'posh'. Children sometimes confuse the two to the extent that they think anything is formal provided it is said in a posh accent! Instead, as they undertake this unit, children should be focused upon the extra effort required to understand more formal language. This will be seen in the incomprehensibility of some of the legal snippets they could find if they cut law reports out of a newspaper.

About the activities
Photocopiable: Who writes what?
The uses of language described in the photocopiable can be matched up to the snippets from various texts. Children can look out for levels of formality and clues within the language to decide which text is which.

Photocopiable: Formal contract
This is a mock up of a formal contract. Children can read it, section by section, and try figuring out what each section is saying. They can also look for, and circle, technical vocabulary and unfamiliar words and look these up in a dictionary. This photocopiable can be used in conjunction with the photocopiable 'Contract words'. The children should be given the table as another activity adding on to the undertaking of the reading of the contract already undertaken.

Photocopiable: Contract words
Having come to this contract 'cold' this photocopiable provides some guidance to three of the sections. Children could use some of the language and try to devise sentences and contracts of their own. They could draw up an agreement with their teacher (extra playtime in return for extra effort?). The teacher can discuss ideas for contracts and children can draw on this photocopiable for terms like 'hereinafter' and 'indemnify'.

Following up
Collect formalities: Children can collect formal notices and letters from parents and other adults and look at some of the language used in this. Letters of various kinds can be looked at along with postcards, e-mails and junk mail. Children can try putting into their own words the characteristics of these pieces of writing.

Contract writing: Children can try drawing up their own contracts between different parties, such as an agreement to keep the classroom tidy. They can use some of the language used in the book contract shown.

Who writes what?

❑ Look at these sections from letters and notes and see if you can match the text to the description.

Am I the only reader who is angry about the road works in the centre of town?

Round at Josh's. See you at 5.00.

I have had a good weekend, reading books and watching television. Very relaxing.

WISH YOU WERE HERE. THE SUN IS BRILLIANT!

It is of the utmost importance that you contact me as soon as possible to discuss your financial arrangements.

Take a look at our brochure. We offer sun, sea and adventure. Whatever you are looking for next **Summer – we'll look after you**.

It was just what I wanted and was so surprised. Thanks again, Sam.

Oh, Juliet. You are like the sun. Please, please reply soon.

❑ Match up pairs and stick them onto a sheet of paper.

descriptions

letter of complaint to a local newspaper	a love letter!
letter from a bank manager to someone who owes the bank money	letter from a holiday company advertising their holidays
note between two friends	note left on fridge from a boy to his mum
postcard from a holiday	Thank you letter from a child to his granny

Formal contract

Memorandum of agreement made between William Shakespeare (hereinafter termed 'the author') of the one part and Fantastic Publications (hereinafter termed 'the publishers') of the other part.

The author herein grants the exclusive right of publishing the work "A Midsummer Night's Dream – the Return", (hereinafter termed 'the work').

Two copies of the work shall be delivered to the publisher on or before 29th February 2001.

The publishers shall undertake, with due diligence, to publish the work within 18 months of delivery of the complete typescript unless they are prevented from doing so by strikes, fire, flood, lockouts or other circumstances beyond their reasonable control.

The publishers undertake that the author's name shall appear in its customary form and with due prominence on the front cover and title page of every copy of the work.

The publishers agree to pay the author an advance in anticipation of monies that may become due to the author under this agreement the sum of £1,000,000.

It is agreed that the author shall receive 10% of the cover price of all copies sold.

It is agreed that if the publishers consider their exclusive rights to the said work have been infringed by another party they shall be at liberty to take such steps as they may consider necessary for dealing with the matter, undertaking to pay all costs in this matter and to indemnify the author against all liability for costs.

I. Hawk

Will Shakespeare

Contract words

❑ Use this table to help you understand some of the sections of the formal contract.

Memorandum of agreement made between William Shakespeare (hereinafter termed 'the author') of the one part and Fantastic Publications (hereinafter termed 'the publishers') of the other part.	This section states who the parties to the agreement are and what the play is called: 'hereinafter' means 'from this point forwards'.
The publishers shall undertake, with due diligence, to publish the work within 18 months of delivery of the complete typescript unless they are prevented from doing so by strikes, fire, flood, lockouts or other circumstances beyond their reasonable control.	In this section the publishers give the time by which they aim to publish the play. 'With due diligence' means 'with the right amount of care'; unless they are prevented from doing so' means 'unless something stops them'. 'Circumstances beyond their reasonable control' means 'something happening they couldn't expect or control'.
It is agreed that if the publishers consider their exclusive rights to the said work have been infringed by another party they shall be at liberty to take such steps as they may consider necessary for dealing with the matter, undertaking to pay all costs in this matter and to indemnify the author against all liability for costs.	The publishers are saying that if someone else publishes the play they will take them to court. If they do this, the writer won't have to pay for the court case. 'Exclusive rights' means these publishers are the only ones allowed to publish the play; 'infringed' means 'ignored and broken'; 'at liberty' means 'free'; 'such steps as they may consider necessary' means 'whatever they think needs to be done'; and 'indemnify' means 'protect'.

Formal letters

Objective
Discuss and experiment with the use of formal language

Language issues
There are a number of conventions used in the writing of formal letters. These include the placing of the address and date. There are also differences in the type of language used in formal letters. The informal note will just say 'See you Saturday' whereas the formal letter is most likely to dress this up: 'If it is convenient we would like you to attend a meeting on Saturday...'

Ways of teaching
Bear in mind that the aim of this unit is not to become etiquette-ridden letter writers! The letters are examples of a type of language use children are exploring, namely the level of formality. By replying to letters and figuring out who would have written different letter types children can explore the continuum that lies between the very formal letter and the scrappy, informal note.

About the activities
Photocopiable: Write to reply
Replies are matched to the letters to which they reply. This activity provides children with a range of different types of communication. In replying they must decide the tone of their reply, how formal or informal it will be and so on.

Photocopiable: Formal letter
The conventions shown are typical of the sort of brief handed out in careers lessons, council offices and so on to explain how a formal letter is to be presented. People tinker with the conventions all the time but, using this one as a model, children could try a letter writing activity of their own (see 'Following up' suggestions).

Photocopiable: Letter heading
Using the letter headings children can step into the role outlined and let their imagination run riot. They may want to anticipate questions their addressee will raise and tackle any objections they see (for example – how will the headteacher react to longer holidays?)

Following up
Etiquette!: Books of etiquette and some dictionaries contain interesting and slightly dated details about modes of address. They explain things like how to address an 'Earl' and who, exactly, should be referred to as 'Your Royal Highness'. Children can have a look at such lists and find some of the different formal modes.

Letter writing: Children can try writing some formal letters to someone like their local MP or a broadcasting company. These could be written making a request. For example, manufacturers and distributors involved in a business linked to a topic can be asked to send promotional posters and material.

Note chat: Children can try having a conversation by note. They sit either side of the table and don't speak! Instead they write notes to each other. As the activity progresses they might start to abbreviate and rush things.

Write to reply

❏ Write a short reply to each of the following texts.

Hi, Thought we could do something this Saturday. Any ideas? Leave a note on my desk with any thoughts. Be in touch, see ya,	
PUBLIC NOTICE. Permission has been requested for the building of twenty modern, luxury flats on the site formerly deemed to be the school playground. Those wishing to register objections to these plans should contact *The Planning Officer, Planning Office, Town Hall* on or before the last Thursday of this month.	
Supertoys *Executive Post:* *Computer Game Tester* *Starting salary £500,000 pa.* Supertoys are seeking to expand their team of Computer Game testers. The job is a demanding one – testers have to try out all new computer games. Applications are sought from computer game players between 7 and 11 yrs of age. Please send a short note presenting your suitability for the post. This is your chance to join our team and make 'Supertoys' the best computer game company on the planet!	

Formal letter

This is the conventional way of laying out a formal letter. Can you use this model to make up your own formal letter?

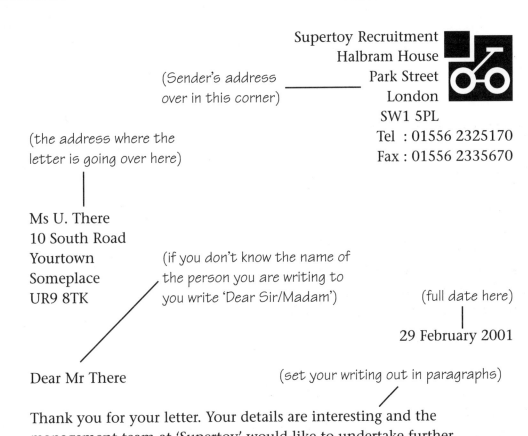

Supertoy Recruitment
Halbram House
Park Street
London
SW1 5PL
Tel : 01556 2325170
Fax : 01556 2335670

(Sender's address over in this corner)

(the address where the letter is going over here)

Ms U. There
10 South Road
Yourtown
Someplace
UR9 8TK

(if you don't know the name of the person you are writing to you write 'Dear Sir/Madam')

(full date here)

29 February 2001

Dear Mr There

(set your writing out in paragraphs)

Thank you for your letter. Your details are interesting and the management team at 'Supertoy' would like to undertake further discussion.

You are invited to visit our company and discuss your suitability for the post. Please ring me to arrange a suitable date for this arrangement.

Yours sincerely

(if you do not know the name of the person you are writing to you end the letter 'Yours faithfully')

W.E.Play

Personnel manager

Please illustrate a piece of paper at the size shown

Letter heading

Formal letters often come on official notepaper.

❑ Cut out an use one of the letter headings below to make your own headed notepaper and try writing one of the letters described in the 'letter brief'.

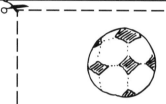

Premier Association
1 Main Street,
London,
W1 0AA

Letter brief:
You are a manager setting up a new football team. You are writing to another manager to try and buy some of her or his players.

The Broadcasting Corporation
3 Main Street,
London,
W1 0AA

Letter brief:
You are a producer making a new pop show. You are writing to a pop star to ask them on the show and tell them what you want.

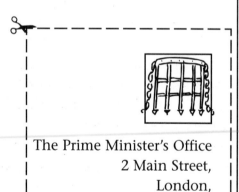

The Prime Minister's Office
2 Main Street,
London,
W1 0AA

Letter brief:
You are the Prime Minister and you have decided to extend the school holidays. You are writing to all headteachers to inform them.

Complexities in sentences

Contents of Term 2b

Unit 1:
Complex sentences   Revise work on complex sentences

Unit 2:
Connecting clauses   Review ways of connecting clauses

Unit 3:
Conditionals   Investigate and use conditionals

Unit 4:
Modal verbs   Investigate and use modal verbs, such as might, could, would

Unit 5:
Contracting sentences   Revise work on contracting sentences and note making

This half-term

This half-term develops the unit on clauses and works its way through some of the complex ways in which sentences can be connected. This includes looking at the conditionals and modal verbs.

Poster notes

A clause
When it comes to giving definitions clauses are difficult to clarify. The poster gives a working definition. There will be exceptions to the rule and a whole host of elements are taken under the general category of 'words linked to that verb'. However, the verb is the important thing for children to look for in their delineating of clauses within sentences – as is emphasized in this poster.

Modal verbs
This plain list of the modal verbs will assist children to recognize the basic list of the ones used in English. It will particularly support work in Unit 4.

A clause

A clause is a group of words including a **verb** and a **subject**
and other words linked to that verb.

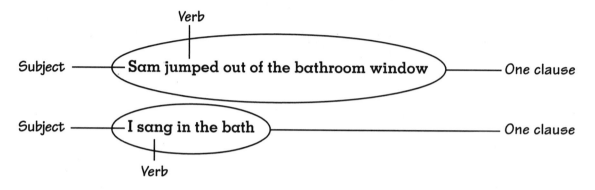

One sentence can have more than one clause.

Sam jumped out of the window because I sang in the bath.

One clause   Another clause

Some sentences contain just one clause.

Sam jumped out of the window.
I sang in the bath.

The modal verbs

would	might	should
may	must	could
will	shall	can

I might fly aeroplanes

I shall be a solicitor

I would like to be a teacher

I could be a scientist

I should like to become a writer

I may be a designer

I can be a dancer

I will be a footballer

Complex sentences

Objective
Revise work on complex sentences

Language issues
The addition of clauses can make a simple sentence into a complex or compound one.

Beginning with a simple sentence, for example 'The cat ran.' This is a simple, single clause sentence. In a complex sentence a subordinate clause is added to a simple, main clause.

Subordinate clauses make sense in relation to the main clause. They say something about it and are dependent upon it. Take the following examples: 'The cat ran because the dog barked' and 'The cat ran when he saw the dog'. In both these cases the subordinate clause ('because the dog barked', 'when he saw the dog') is actually elaborating on the main clause. They are typically introduced by words like 'because' and 'when', showing that what follows tells the reader more about the main clause.

Compound sentences contain more than one clause, but the clauses are of equal significance and none are subordinate. For example: 'The little dog laughed and the dish ran away.' Both pieces of information are of equal importance and neither is dependent upon the other.

Ways of teaching
The teacher should encourage the understanding that although they are a difficult subject in theory, clauses usually ornament, add interest to and ultimately enhance a writer's style.

About the activities
Photocopiable: Clause or not?
As a way of looking at the definition and understanding of the term 'clause' this activity asks children to sort bits of sentences that are complete clauses from bits that are not. There are two guidelines to draw to their attention as children undertake this task. Firstly, a clause is very much like a little sentence, indeed simple sentences consist of one clause. Secondly a clause contains a verb. By looking for a chunk that functions independently with a verb children should be able to pick out the clauses.

Photocopiable: Find the main clause
This activity introduces the idea of main clauses as opposed to subordinate clauses. This is a difficult idea and there are some grammatical pointers to distinguishing the two. However, this activity depends to a large extent on children figuring out what the main action of the sentence is. Point out that main clauses can appear at the beginning or end of a sentence.

Once they have isolated the subordinate clause they might be able to discuss how the subordinate adds to the main clause. Does it explain when the main clause was done, or why, or how?

Photocopiable: The Princess and the Pea 1889
This old rendition of a well known story gives children a chance to encounter varied sentence constructions and to try and find various clauses. Once again, looking for a verb is given as a way of tracking down clauses.

Following up
Historical texts: Children can look at examples of texts in history books and classic literature to examine the prevalence of more complex sentences. Are older texts more or less likely to contain complex sentences?

Reviewing writing: Looking at their own story writing and work in other subject areas, children can consider whether they are now using a range of different types of sentence. They may find places in their work where they could have and places where it would have improved their writing.

Clause or not?

Clauses are distinct parts of a sentence. They contain a verb.
They can look like a sentence. For example this sentence:

| I will see you when I get a chance after I eat my tea. |

contains three clauses:

| I will see you | when I get a chance | after I eat my tea. |

each of which has its own verb and makes sense.

| I will see you. | | when I get a chance. | | after I eat my tea. |

❏ In the sentences below some strings of words are underlined. Some of the circled bits are clauses. Some are not. Can you sort the clauses from the non-clauses?

	Clause	Not a clause
<u>Jamie ran away</u> and he hid in the tree house.		
<u>The little, green, house</u> is very old.		
My friend made a cake but <u>it tasted horrible</u>.		
My <u>best friend in the whole</u> school is leaving!		
<u>My Gran says</u> she was around before the dinosaurs.		
<u>One of the children let off a stink bomb</u> and it made the whole playground smell.		
<u>Every Saturday my sister works on her motorbike</u> then she goes out for a ride.		

Find the main clause

In sentences like this:

> **We played outside after we finished our tea.**

there is a main clause:

> *We played outside* after we finished our tea.

This bit tells you when we did the main bit.

This is the main thing stated in the sentence.

Other bits, like this | We played outside *after we finished our tea.* | called subordinate clauses.

They are linked to the main clause and tell us a bit more about it.
The main clause is the main thing the sentence has to say.
It makes sense on its own.

❑ Look at these sentences and sort the main clauses from subordinating clauses.
Circle the main clauses in red and subordinating clauses in blue.

We played outside when the rain stopped.

I made my tea because I was hungry.

Because we were good this morning we got five minutes extra play.

Mum bought a motorbike so she could visit Gran.

The aeroplane took off after everyone was on board.

We are careful when we cross the main road.

Our teacher went home because he was ill.

The caretaker took us outside to teach us some football skills.

Because it was raining we stayed indoors.

Since we started school in September we've been on three trips.

While we were waiting for the bus we played a game of catch.

The garden was ruined after the cows trampled through it.

The Princess and the Pea, 1889

❑ Look at this passage from Andrew Lang's "The Princess on the Pea" (as it was originally called), first published in 1899. The sentences are long and complex. Can you find and circle 25 different clauses? Make a list of the verbs in each of these clauses.

There was once a prince who wanted a princess, but she'd got to be a real princess. So he travelled round the whole world just to find such a one – but everywhere there was something wrong. Certainly, there were plenty of princesses, but he could never quite make up his mind if they were real princesses for there was always something that didn't seem quite right about them. So he came home again, all sad, because he wanted to have a true princess.

One evening a fearful storm blew up – thunder, lightning, rain streaming down – it was absolutely terrible! Then there came a knocking on the town-gate and the old King went down himself to open it.

It was a princess, standing out there. But, goodness gracious, what a sight she was in the rain and the storm! The water ran down her hair and down her clothes, and it ran into the toes of her shoes and out at the heels, and yet she said she was a true princess.

"Huh, we'll soon see about that!" thought the old Queen, but she didn't say it out loud. She just went into the bed-chamber, took off all the bed-clothes and put a pea on the bottom of the bedstead; then she took twenty mattresses and put them on top of the pea, and then she put twenty eiderdown quilts on top of the mattress.

That's where the princess had to lie all night.

Next morning they asked her how she'd slept.

"Oh it was terrible," said the princess. "I hardly shut my eyes the whole night long! God knows what was in my bed. There was something so hard in there that I'm black and blue all over! It really was absolutely terrible!"

So they could see that she was a real princess, because she'd felt the pea through those twenty mattresses and twenty eiderdown quilts. Only a true princess could have such delicate skin.

The prince took her for his queen, for now he knew that she was a real princess, and the pea ended up in the art gallery where you can still see it unless someone's taken it away.

There now – that was a real story.

Connecting clauses

Objective
Review ways of connecting clauses

Language issues
In compound and complex sentences various connecting words either link or subordinate one clause to another.

Compound sentences typically link clauses with words like 'and' or 'but'. They use conjunctions that add or oppose two clauses – for example, 'I like coffee and I like strawberries.', 'Josh wanted to play but Chloe wanted to read.'

In *complex* sentences one clause is dependent upon another and is typically introduced by a conjunction like 'because' or 'when', as in: 'The children lined up because the bell rang.' (The relationship in compound sentences is one of co-ordination between clauses whereas in complex sentences it is one of subordination.)

Clauses can also be marked out by punctuation, so the above could be separated by commas: 'The children lined up, the bell rang' or semicolons: 'Josh wanted to play; Chloe wanted to read.'

Ways of teaching
The focus in this unit is upon the connection of clauses. Each of the photocopiables places before children a set of sentences in which they have to consider where or how the clauses connect. As they do this their work should be supported by the encouragement to try picking out the clauses in the sentences with which they are working.

About the activities
Photocopiable: Finish the sentence
By finishing the sentences children have to consider the content of the first clause but they also have to look at the connecting word and assess where it is leading the sentence. They will notice that some of the sentences are identical up to the point at which the connection is made. It will be interesting to compare the way in which differences at this point lead to different clauses.

Photocopiable: Sentences in pieces
In this activity children find the right word to connect clauses together and rebuild the story. The completed version should read: 'There was a problem when we got home. We switched on the lights but they were not working. Dad called an electrician because he couldn't mend the lights. The electrician said she could fix things; however she said it would take a while. We stayed with our neighbour until the problem was fixed. Eventually the problem was fixed so we went home.'

Photocopiable: Punctuating complex sentences
Through a process of elimination children can work out where to place the punctuation marks between the clauses in these sentences. Point out that the marks are between clauses, this may help children to work out which ones to discard and which to retain.

Following up
Change connectives: Children can look in texts and find complex sentences with connectives linking the clauses. They can try a different connective to link the two (see the 'Ways of connecting' poster for examples).

Connective jobs: Looking at a range of texts promoting or advertising different things, whether it be houses or holidays, children can look at the connecting language used and see how it links clauses – for example: 'Is one clause being used to explain or support another?'

Finish the sentence

❑ Look at these sentences. Can you think of clauses that could end these sentences?

We waited for the bus and

I am going to visit my friend although

Sam wrote a letter and

Sam wrote a letter because

We waited for the bus because

We waited for the bus but

We planned a game of football however

We planned a game of football so

I am going to visit my friend unless

We waited for the bus until

Sam wrote a letter when

I am going to visit my friend while

Sentences in pieces

Different words can join one clause to another.

❑ Match up the beginnings and endings of these sentences and find the right connecting word to put between them. Try rebuilding the story.

There was a problem
We switched on the lights
Dad called an electrician
The electrician said she could fix things
We stayed with our neighbour
Eventually the problem was fixed

when	because	but

so	until	however

they were not working.
the problem was fixed.
we got home.
she said it would take a while.
we went home.
he couldn't mend the lights.

Punctuating complex sentences

Between two clauses you can have a comma, separating them:

> Walking in the park, I saw a lion.

or a semicolon.

> The lion was in the park; he goes there everyday.

❑ Each of these sentences has too many commas or semicolons. Can you rewrite them?
Leave out two that shouldn't be there and keep the one that should.

The comma tells the reader to pause between the clauses.

The semicolon separates clauses that are closely related.

Walking in; the park, I saw; a lion.	
The lion was in; the park; he goes, there everyday.	
Crossing the road, I slipped; on; the ice.	
Chloe was late; for school; she always, is.	
I, bought, this vase, it cost £100.	
We queued, for ages; we were; freezing cold.	
Our flat is; great; it's got a good; view.	
I wanted; to watch; the cartoons; my sister wanted football.	
Come and, visit us, call in any, time.	
Some days it, rains; some days, it doesn't.	

Conditionals

Objective
Investigate and use conditionals

Language issues
Conditionals, as the name suggests, present the conditions for a particular action or happening. They are clauses that place a condition on the activity in the main verb of a sentence – for example, 'If the clock strikes twelve, you must come home.' The conditionals are the 'if...' part of such sentences. The sentence isn't just an instruction 'you must come home'; it is subject to the condition.

The conditional clause is a type of subordinate clause. The clause 'If the clock strikes twelve' is subordinate to the main clause. As with all subordinate clauses it makes no sense on its own but is providing the conditions for the main clause: 'you must come home'. Other examples of this usage include: 'Unless you leave I shall call the police', 'Should you run into Chloe, tell her I'll be late.'

Ways of teaching
In teaching about conditionals we are asking children to look at an arrangement in language that links to a way of thinking. The emphasis throughout this unit is upon the way in which one thing depends upon another and the implications that has for deduction, speculation and supposition.

About the activities
Photocopiable: Conditions
After creating various conditional sentences children can grade the likelihood of their examples. How likely is it that the 'If' part will come true? They can give three stars to the likely, two to the less likely and one to the unlikely.

Photocopiable: Speculations
As children speculate upon the possible outcome of events in various stories, they might be encouraged to devise alternative endings to well known tales. They could write a 'Cinderella' without the prince. She might even live happier ever after!

Photocopiable: Two doorkeepers
'The two doorkeepers' is a classic puzzle involving conditions and deduction. Children must think of a question and ask one doorkeeper but must then consider how the question will be answered by reasoning: 'If this is the liar he will say...' and 'If this is the one who tells the truth he will say...'.

So a question like 'Does the west door lead to certain doom?' doesn't help because the liar will lie and the one telling the truth will tell the truth – but you don't know which one is which.

Asking 'Are you the liar?' won't help either. The liar will say 'No'. So will the one who tells the truth.

Baffled? The solution is given in 'Following up'.

Following up
The solution: the answer to 'The two doorkeepers' provides even more of a chance to think in 'If...then...' terms.

The question to ask0 either of them is a question about what the other one would say.
Ask 'Lefty' this:
'If I asked Righty "Which door leads to the good road ahead?" what would he say?'
Listen to the answer. Whichever door he says – go through the other one.
Reason it through...
If the one you asked was the liar then he knows the other one would tell the truth.
If the other one would tell the truth he would say the right door.
The liar will lie about what the truth teller would say.
If the one you asked tells the truth then he knows the other one would lie.
If the other one would lie then the door he says would really be the wrong one.
The question works, whichever one you are talking to!

Conditions

❏ Look at these conditional sentences.

If	the sun sets	then	it will be dark.
If	I lose my pocket money	then	I won't be able to spend it.
If	my Mum has to work tonight	then	I will have to stay with Gran.

❏ Using the model below, try creating your own examples of conditionals.

If		then	
If		then	
If		then	
If		then	
If		then	
If		then	
If		then	
If		then	
If		then	
If		then	

Speculations

In stories, one event depends upon another.
❑ Look at these speculations from two well known stories:

Cinderella If | Cinderella hadn't run out of the palace | then | she might not have left the slipper.

If | Cinderella hadn't left the slipper | then | the Prince would not have found her.

Jack and the Beanstalk If | Jack hadn't sold the cow | then | he wouldn't have got the magic beans.

If | Jack hadn't got the magic beans | then | he wouldn't have grown a beanstalk.

❑ Try making your own speculations from stories you know. Try and think of two for each story.

Story

If | | then |

If | | then |

Story

If | | then |

If | | then |

Two doorkeepers

❏ This is a very old puzzle.

Here are two doors.
One of them leads to a good road ahead.
The other leads to certain doom.
You don't know which one is which.

In front of the door there are two doorkeepers.
One of them always tells the truth.
The other always tells lies.
You don't know which one is which.

They know which door leads to the good road and which leads to certain doom.

You can ask one of the doorkeepers one question. Then you must choose your door, and step through it.

❏ Think about your question.

Modal verbs

Objective
Investigate and use modal verbs, such as 'might', 'could' and would

Language issues
Modal verbs indicate the conditions or likelihood of a main verb. For example, the sentence 'I eat food' is a plain statement of the strong likelihood of an action, whereas 'I might eat food' sounds less likely. It is the modal verb that raises the idea of the necessity or likelihood of an action of it happening.

The modal verbs in English are: would, could, might, should, can, will, shall, may, must. These verbs never function on their own as main verbs. They always act as auxiliaries helping another verb. We can say 'I help' or 'I could help' but 'I could' on its own makes no sense without another verb (or the implicit sense of another verb).

Ways of teaching
The modal verbs are words with which children will be very familiar and use all the time. In this unit they are being asked to hold this usage up to examination. As such, the emphasis is upon them generating and developing their own sentences and ideas using modal verbs with a view towards understanding the function they perform and the differences between them.

About the activities
Photocopiable: Using modal verbs
This exercise asks children to explore possible uses of these words. Children will have used modal verbs extensively in their writing and conversation but this addresses them in isolation as a feature of language.

Photocopiable: In your dreams
By matching situations to particular modals children generate sentences about possible events. One facet of this activity worth exploring is the difference a change of modal can make. For example, the 'If I become a millionaire' may generate a different response for the modal 'I will' and 'I should'. The second might prompt feelings of obligation. Also worth looking out for are the verbs with which children follow the modals to see what actions they plan in each situation.

Photocopiable: Modal degrees
As a way of exploring the differences between modals this activity leads children to use different modals in different ways. In doing so it explores how probable and certain the various modals are. Children may debate which statements they think they can make under each heading. They often end up philosophically asking whether anything is certain!

Following up
Listen for modals: Children can listen to extracts of television and radio news and try to spot the use of modals. Items involving interviews with politicians can be a gem in this activity, particularly when the interviewer is trying to tie them down to a 'Will you...? 'and the politician will only offer a 'We should....' or 'We might...' in response.

Predictions: Using modal verbs children can make predictions about future events in a story they are reading or a series they are following on the television. As in the 'Modal degrees' activity they can try to rate the likelihood of events.

Using modal verbs

Modal verbs change main verbs.

In front of a verb like: | I run. |

you can place a modal verb: | I **could** run. |

to show how likely or unlikely the verb is: | I will run **if** I am late. |

or how certain or uncertain it is. | I **might** run in the race tomorrow. |

❑ Use each of these modal verbs in a sentence. Try to use each of the modal verbs below.

Modal verbs

| would | could | might | should | can | will | shall | may | must |

1 _____

2 _____

3 _____

4 _____

5 _____

6 _____

7 _____

8 _____

9 _____

In your dreams

Modal verbs can be used to show things we will do, or could do.
❑ Match the situations below with a modal verb.

If I become Prime Minister	I will

Finish off the sentence.

If I become Prime Minister	I will	*extend the school holidays.*

Write the full sentence down on another sheet of paper.

Situations	**Modals**
If I become a millionaire	I would
If I became Prime Minister	I could
If I get shipwrecked on a desert island	I might
When I am old enough to do a job	I should
If I became famous	I can
When I move into my own house	I will
When I can go on holiday by myself	I shall
When I can choose a pet of my own	I may

Modal degrees

Some modals say things are sure to happen.
The rain **will** stop at some time.

Some say they are likely.
It **should** brighten up later on.

Some just say they could happen.
It **might** stop before playtime.

❑ Try to think up some things that definitely will or won't happen tomorrow:
It will...   **I shall...**   **My teacher won't...**

some things that are likely to happen tomorrow:
It should....   **I should....**

and some things that might or might not happen tomorrow.
We might...   **I could....**

some things that definitely will or won't happen tomorrow	some things that are likely to happen tomorrow	some things that might or might not happen tomorrow

Contracting sentences

Objective
Revise work on contracting sentences and note making

Language issues
Contractions of sentences can be used for note taking purposes, to create headlines or to summarize story contents in a blurb. In such cases the context of the contracted form or understanding of the reader should enable access to the sentence's meaning. Such sentences do leave themselves open to ambiguity. When sentences are contracted there is a need for balance between an effective decrease in the number of words and a point where the original is still recoverable. It is no good eliminating so many words that the message is lost. On the other hand if too many are left in a set of notes there was no point summarizing.

Ways of teaching
The three activities in this unit play around with genuine note taking situations. The focus should be upon looking at the information that is absolutely necessary to tell a story. What type of word carries the important information? What do the children need to listen out for as they make their notes?

About the activities
Photocopiable: Notes to sentences
This activity involves children in making journalist style notes about an item of news. It is best approached using short news items taped from a radio broadcast, preferably a pop channel with news that will interest the children.

Once they have made their notes they can compare with a partner to see whether they missed anything out.

They can also look at the type of word it was most useful to scribble down to retain the main content of the story; this is perhaps the area where there should be the least disagreement.

Photocopiable: Rebuild the sentence
This activity consists of note taking in reverse: as they undertake this activity children are asked to rebuild the original sentences and events from the notes. The teacher could stagger the distribution of the notes, giving children one set at a time and letting them build up the story. Alternatively they could work with all three, reconstructing the sequence of events.

Photocopiable: Editing
This is a badly written account of events. The editing activity has two parts to it. Children can find words that could be cut from the sentences in the text. They can also look at ways of rewriting some of the sentences in fewer words. The ultimate challenge is to see if they can reduce the text to 200 words, retaining the important facts and quotes.

Following up
Newspaper counts: Looking at a short news story chosen from a newspaper, children can try to rewrite the same story using fewer words.

Trail making: Following on from 'Rebuild the sentence', children can try to create their own story in note form. One group could try to set an example of a story in note form for another group and see if the latter can solve it. This could be a famous narrative or a story they make up.

Notes to sentences

❏ Listen to two items of news from the radio. As you listen, make notes about them.

❏ Using your notes, try to write some sentences about each story.

What sort of words did you have in your notes? Compare your notes with a friend – did you miss any crucial words?

Rebuild the sentence

Our investigator has gone missing and left some pages of her notepad.
❑ Looking at the notes can you reconstruct what might have happened in her last few hours? Any ideas where she might be?

1.00 p.m.
robbery – main bank
called by Mr Sneak (manager)

robbers used back window – LEFT OPEN!
Why?

Mr Sneak not want answer questions

asked to leave   5.30pm
watched bank

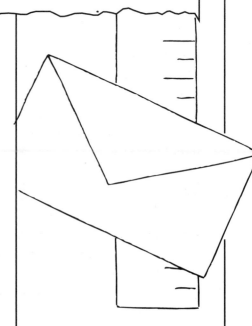

Sneak leaves 5.10
followed him

Sneak to "Arnie's Cafe"

Sneak meets man
Sneak calls him "Mr Bigg"

They agree – meet at statue 6.00.

Bigg leaves.
Sneak – tea (scrambled eggs , toast)   6.10pm
Sneak and Bigg meet at statue

Man gives Sneak £10,000!
Says "Thanks for your help – that window's a tight squeeze."

Bigg plans to leave country.
Sneak: "I'll come with you – just go home get pet – "Fluffy"
Bigg: "Got 20 minutes".

Who to follow?

FOLLOW SNEAK – HOME

You could write a report of your thoughts on a separate sheet of paper.

Editing

This newspaper story is too long. You are the editor.
❑ Find words that can be cut out. How many can you cut?
  The current story is 300 words long. Can you tell the story in 200 words?

The respectable, sleepy, little town of Sallyhampton was deeply shocked yesterday to hear of a really massive and nasty criminal operation in its very own High Street. Investigative reporter, Irrum Hassan, uncovered a very serious plot by the manager of the local bank, who is called Ian Sneak.

Following yesterday's burglary, reported in this paper, Ms Hassan trailed the bank manager wherever he went around town. "I had my suspicions," she said. "I never trust someone with a brightly coloured tie."

Hassan trailed Sneak all the way to the "Arnie's Cafe", a well known haunt of criminals who are in the town, and there she witnessed him liaising with a thief, Vic Bigg. What emerged while she was watching them in the cafe was a conspiracy in which Sneak had left a bank window open, allowing Bigg to enter the bank and steal £20,000.

Intrepid Hassan followed Sneak and Bigg to another meeting later on at which the bank manager was paid money totalling £10,000 for his services in the robbery. After all this had happened Hassan then followed Sneak home, where the rogue bank manager proceeded to pack his bags with the intention of fleeing the country.

By now it was too late to turn back. While observing Sneak, Hassan was caught by the bank manager and locked down in the cellar of his house.

It was only the work of Hassan's colleagues, piecing together her notes, that made it possible for police from the police station to swoop upon Sneak's house.

They apprehended the bank manager who was in the house and then the police who had gone to the house saved Hassan from being fed to his pet crocodile, Fluffy.

When asked how they figured out her whereabouts, Hassan's colleagues commented that "It's all a matter of grammar."

Text types

Contents of Term 3a

This half-term

The units in this half-term step beyond sentence level work into looking at the way language is structured in a range of texts. The promotion of a wide range of types of writing has been a feature of recent innovations in the primary curriculum. While there are many features about purpose and audience that affect the way such text types are constructed, this set of units maintains a focus upon the grammar of varying text types. A full and useful analysis of varying text types can be found in *Developing Children's Non-fiction Writing* by Lewis and Wray (Scholastic).

Poster notes

Sentence functions
This poster gives examples of sentences in various types of text. As there are texts that recount and explain so there are also certain types of sentence construction that figure prominently within such texts.

Discussion chart
The discussion chart provides a frame within which different sides of a discussion can be organized. As an A3 poster it can be filled in with an issue such as 'Should school start an hour earlier and end an hour earlier?' and the two sides can be argued with the main points being noted in each of the columns.

Sentence functions

Sentences can do a variety of things. They can:

Function	Text example	For example:
Recount an event	I went to the park.	In a diary
Narrate a story	A goblin stole a bicycle and rode away quickly.	In an illustrated story book or novel
Give an instruction	Glue the paper to the card.	On an instruction leaflet with a diagram
Report on something	The school is three storeys high and has a very tall bell tower.	Typed as an official report
Explain things	The heat of the sun evaporates the water in the puddle.	Written with a diagram in a science book
Try and persuade the reader	The council should reject plans to build the new road across the woods.	As a protest leaflet
Discuss an issue	Some people think cars are good but others say they harm the environment.	Written as a newspaper editorial

Discussion chart

The issue:

One side	Another side

Conclusion

The language of text types

Objective
Examine the grammatical conventions of different types of texts

Language issues
As various texts are produced to serve different purposes, they become clustered together into groups with certain similarities. The inherent similarities between certain types of text in each of these groups leads, over time, to them being understood as belonging to a particular genre. This term is derived from the Latin 'genus', the root word from which words like 'genetics' are derived. This can provide a useful way of thinking about genres in that they are the familial relationships that link together certain texts. Texts that give instructions, texts that sell a product, texts that worship a deity – all these will show similarities that enable us to categorize them together within a 'genre'. The term is particularly well-known from cinema, where genres such as comedy and thriller are used to categorize various films (and to organize video hire shops!).

Obviously texts of a certain genre can be linked by similar content (such as the love element common to romantic fiction). However, there are two other features relevant to our work on sentences that contribute to the links between texts. Firstly, the way in which the texts are structured will follow certain patterns, both in the overall layout of the page and the type of sentence used. For example, questionnaires are normally structured as lists with questions whereas recipes include a list followed by a paragraph of directions. Secondly the texts will use certain types of language. An example of this is the use of first person verbs in the past tense when writing personal narratives.

There are variations within different texts but general ideas of how different text types are structured can be informed by a grasp of sentence grammar.

Ways of teaching
The main aim of this unit is to open up the whole idea of the language of texts. By this stage in their learning many children will have experienced the reading and writing of texts such as persuasive pieces and procedural instructions.

At the outset of a unit that focuses upon the sentence-level aspects of these varied text types the unit explores snippets of texts and ways of writing with the aim of focusing children upon the link between text type and language convention.

About the activities
Photocopiable: Different text snippets
Text snippets in the photocopiable are cut free from any title or context. Ideas of where these texts come from or what they are about will be formed as children link the language in the snippets with the things they know about texts. Watch out for the detail in their guesses as they make links. Push for the maximum level of guesswork. If a child suggests a snippet is from a letter, ask what sort. If they say it is a complaint, ask who it is to.

Photocopiable: Ways of writing
The type of language used in certain types of text emerges when children try to write different texts. The main point in this activity is that they are asked to try different types of text in close proximity to each other. As they do this, encourage them to look out for changes in the type of sentence they use and the way they form their verbs.

Photocopiable: The jobs texts do
This activity focuses upon the functions of texts. It is well supported by the poster 'Text types'. The types described are significant categories. There are texts that will draw upon more than one of the functions listed; for example, a political speech may include anecdotal story mixed with report followed by persuasion. If children approach mixed texts, encourage them to focus upon a sentence or set of sentences to look at their function.

Following up
Text detective: Children can make their own detective game by cutting snippets out of texts and setting them for other children to guess as much as they can about their origin. The skill in this is largely on the part of the snippers! They have to strike a balance between getting enough text to make the task possible and too much, making it too easy.

Snippet collection: Children can collect good examples of language use in different types of text and build up a collection of snippets on large sheets of paper. Different sheets can be used for different types of text and examples can be clipped out of leaflets and magazines.

Switching style: Children can try to rewrite a text in one style as a text in another. How would they write an instructional version of 'The Three Bears'? (First take a Little Girl, then add on cottage). Could they write a recipe in a persuasive way (You must crack the eggs because...)?

Different text snippets

❑ Look at these extracts. They are from different texts. Can you work out what type of text they are from? Note down the clues that helped you figure this out.

The extracts are:	I think this is from....	My clues are...
Move your counter along the board, the number of spaces shown on the dice.		
If your parents let you visit next weekend we could repair the old go-kart.		
In a surprise announcement yesterday, the Prime Minister announced new measures to tackle crime.		
Fry the onion until it is soft then add the mushrooms.		
The sun, the sea, the fun – they are all part of our holiday package for you.		
Chips 90p Curry Sauce 75p Fishcake £1.00		
The castle walls date back to the 13th century though some sections are thought to be much older.		
The light shines through the prism and is refracted into the various colours of the spectrum.		
But if you leave me I'll just go back to the start Just close the door Because it will break my heart.		

Ways of writing

❑ Try writing three sentences you would use to start these pieces of writing.

Your life story	The instructions for playing a game
An advert persuading someone to buy cabbage	**An explanation of how a bike works**

❑ Look at the verbs you used and the type of sentences you wrote. Make some notes about the differences in the way you did the four pieces of writing.

Notes about the differences

The jobs texts do

Sentences perform various functions. They can:

recount an event
narrate a story
give an instruction
report on something
explain things
try and persuade the reader
discuss an issue.

Find an example sentence that really does the job!

❑ Find some examples of different texts. Fill in this table showing
- what text it is
- what job you think it does
- a sentence that shows the text doing its job.

Text	Job it does	Example sentence
Complaining letter	Recounts bad things that happened and asks for money back	"When we switched it on water poured out of the load pipe and flooded the kitchen floor"

Text	Job it does	Example sentence

Narratives and recounts

Objective

Examine the grammatical conventions of narrative and recount texts

Language issues

Narratives and text that recount events are usually structured in chronological form. The text is structured in a way that arranges activities over linear time and contains sentences in which actions and happenings are described. There are examples of narratives written in the present tense, such as jokes in which the 'Three men are walking down a street and they see this...' type of sentence is quite common. However, narratives typically use past tense verbs:

'Dear Diary, today I visited...'

'Once upon a time a miller lived in a cottage...'

'Yesterday the Prime Minister announced...'

They typically identify the participants involved in the actions and the places in which events took place. What can be seen in the above examples is a clear identification of the participants in the action. Even when represented by a pronoun, as in the diary entry, it is clear who the 'I' is.

Ways of teaching

Children should be extremely familiar with the narrative form. In this unit they are asked to reflect upon the language used in this text type. This unit should work hand in hand with the provision of a chance for them to reflect upon and develop their own reading and writing of narratives and recounts.

About the activities

Photocopiable: Verbs that tell

This activity asks children to look at the type of verb used to communicate action in a piece of story writing. It could be done once without thesauruses and then redrafted with their aid. One suggested set of verbs is shown below.

The outlaw gazed into her eyes.

"Robin" she gasped. "Behind you!"

He swung round as three of the Sheriff's guards hurtled down the steps towards him. They swung their swords over their heads and lunged at the outlaw. Quickly Marion swept him up into her arms and leaped through the castle window, plunging into the moat below.

As they spun down into the murky depths he longed for air but the murky weeds of the moat wrapped around his legs. Suddenly a hand grasped the scruff of his neck and dragged him from the water. Marion bundled him onto her horse and jumped up behind him. They galloped off into the forest. Behind them, the Sheriff screamed to his guards: "Chase after them!".

The weary guards clambered onto their horses and thundered out of the castle.

With their fierce horses the guards galloped closer but, as they entered the forest, Marion seized Robin's hand and grasped the branch of a tree above them. They swung into the tree and hid there. Underneath the Sheriff's guards thundered on after nobody.

"Marion," he sobbed. "You saved me!".

Photocopiable: Word type story planner

This is not a story planner. The ideal piece of planning for a story will focus upon well plotted events and characters. What this photocopiable does is to ask children to focus upon the potential language they could inject into a piece of story writing. It can be used to plan the opening of a story or an atmospheric passage. As they use it children focus upon the types of words they can feed into their writing.

Photocopiable: The way of telling

The passage is from Charles Dickens's *Bleak House*, which is not a piece of children's fiction. However, the setting presented is a powerful evocation of a London scene. Children can be challenged to work out what the sentences are saying and, in doing so, find some of the different word types in the passage.

Note that 'Chancery' was a court at Lincoln's Inn Hall where Dickens worked as a reporter.

Following up

Various stories: Children can look at a range of stories and judge the way in which each of them uses language. Which one contains interesting descriptions? Can they find a text with too many descriptive words? Children should follow this unit with an investigation into the style of different types of story-writing from a range of writers.

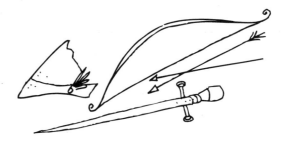

Verbs that tell

❑ Look at the section from the story below. Try to think of a better verb to write over the ones underlined. Remember to use the most dramatic and exciting verbs you can find. Use a thesaurus to help you.

The outlaw <u>looked</u> into her eyes.

"Robin" she <u>said</u>. "Behind you!"

He <u>turned</u> round as three of the Sheriff's guards came down the steps towards him. They <u>had</u> their swords over their heads and <u>went</u> towards the outlaw.

Quickly Marion <u>held</u> him up in her arms and <u>went</u> through the castle window, <u>going</u> into the moat below.

As they <u>went</u> down into the murky depths he <u>hoped</u> for air but the murky weeds of the moat went around his legs. Suddenly a hand <u>held</u> the scruff of his neck and <u>got</u> him from the water. Marion put him onto her horse and <u>went</u> up behind him. They <u>went</u> off into the forest. Behind them, the Sheriff <u>said</u> to his guards "<u>Go</u> after them".

The weary guards <u>went</u> onto their horses and <u>went</u> out of the castle.

With their fierce horses the guards <u>moved</u> closer but, as they entered the forest, Marion <u>held</u> Robin's hand and <u>held</u> the branch of a tree above them. They <u>went</u> into the tree and <u>were</u> there. Underneath the Sheriff's guards <u>moved on</u> after nobody.

"Marion," he sobbed. "You saved me!"

PHOTOCOPIABLE

Word type story planner

❏ Use this planner to think through some of the types of word you will use in a story or a part of a story. It is particularly useful for scary bits, exciting bits, opening bits and romantic bits.

Nouns	Adjective plans	Verb plans	Adverb plans
	Words to describe your noun	*Things your noun does*	*Words to describe how your noun does the verbs*
Someone important			
Something important			
Somewhere important			

The way of telling

❑ Look at this opening section from a classic novel. It is a really difficult passage to read. Have a go!

❑ Look at the choice of verbs. Which nouns grab your attention? Look at some of the adjectives used.

CHAPTER 1

In Chancery

London. Michaelmas term lately over, and the Lord Chancellor sitting in Lincoln's Inn Hall. Implacable November weather. As much mud in the streets, as if the waters had but newly retired from the face of the earth, and it would not be wonderful to meet a Megalosaurus, forty feet long or so, waddling like an elephantine lizard up Holborn Hill. Smoke lowering down from chimney-pots, making a soft black drizzle with flakes of soot in it as big as full-grown snowflakes – gone into mourning, one might imagine, for the death of the sun. Dogs, undistinguishable in mire. Horses, scarcely better; splashed to their very blinkers. Foot passengers, jostling one another's umbrellas, in a general infection of ill temper, and losing their foot-hold at street-corners, where tens of thousands of other foot passengers have been slipping and sliding since the day broke (if this day ever broke), adding new deposits to the crust upon crust of mud, sticking at those points tenaciously to the pavement, and accumulating at compound interest.

❑ Make notes about the words that struck you. What was special about them?

Language notes

Reporting and explaining

Objective
Examine the grammatical conventions of report and explanatory texts

Language issues
Report and explanatory texts outline things for a reader. Explanatory texts map out a process or a system in a way that makes it more understandable to the reader. To do this they identify various components in a process and outline how these interact. These components will often be less personal than in a narrative or recount text. If, for example, a text is explaining how a bill becomes a law in Parliament it will typically refer to impersonal and exemplary participants: 'An MP proposes the bill...', whereas a recount text homes in on an actual happening: 'Today in Parliament the MP for Sheffield North, Katherine Jones, proposed...'

Or compare the sort of language used in an explanation of how a cassette player works – 'The motor turns the cassette tape...' – with the more specific narrative: 'My tape got caught up in my machine.'

In explanatory texts, actions are structured in a way that shows how one action follows (or causes) another and the verbs used are usually in the simple present tense: 'Light shines into the prism…'.

Report texts perform a similar function to explanatory texts but, whereas explanations involve the outlining of a process, report texts present things as they are. An inspection report outlines the current situation that has been inspected. Report texts can be thought of as a picture in words and, as such, use various forms of the verbs 'be' and 'have': 'The school is in a good state of repair', 'The house has a damp proof course...'.

Ways of teaching
Reports and explanations can be quite difficult to distinguish from each other. However the idea of a picture or a process can help children to establish what function a text is performing. Is it reporting a picture or explaining a process?

About the activities
Photocopiable: Links
As children try to explain the processes in this photocopiable they should reflect upon the language they use and the way they structure the writing. Point out the general nature of the explanation many of them should come up with and the way in which a step-by-step process is used to explain what happens.

Photocopiable: Mixed explanations
By picking apart the processes and finding vocabulary they would link together children can rebuild these jumbled explanations. Once they have completed the task they can be asked to mark words and phrases that helped them to identify which sentence belonged where.

Photocopiable: Word pictures
The idea of a word picture is one way of developing children's understanding of the report type of text. As they engage in the subjects given they need to try and stick to the here and now and state how things are. Children often lapse into narrative and can find it useful to think of the difference between a film and a photograph as a way of understanding the nature of the type of writing involved in a report.

Following up
Diagrams: Once they have unjumbled the texts in 'Mixed explanations' children can try to illustrate each with a diagram. In explanatory texts the diagram often maps out a process; children can try a similar type of diagram.

Links

Explanations link things together.

To explain the Solar System I have to tell you how the Earth is guided by the Sun.

To explain how a car works I have to tell you how the petrol connects up to the spark plugs.

❑ Can you try to explain the following things? What process is involved? What words do you use to show how one thing links to another?

Connecting words you might want to use:

when then consequently before after whenever as because so that

Explain how shadows are made

Explain how a pair of scissors works

Mixed explanations

In this text there are three mixed up explanations. Can you pick them apart?
❑ Stick them down on a separate piece of paper and write a title for each explanation.

When something rests in water it pushes water away.

A meteor is a streak of light in the sky caused by a falling object no bigger than a stone.

Whenever you look at something, light bounces off it into your eyes.

As it hurtles towards the earth it burns up.

As it is pushed away the water pushes back.

It then passes through the pupil: the black hole in the middle of your eye.

If the push back is strong enough to support the object it floats.

While travelling towards earth a meteor can reach speeds of 50km per second.

After passing through the pupil it reaches special cells at the back of your eye.

So a heavy ship pushes away a lot of water.

Because of the trail of light meteors are sometimes called 'shooting stars'.

Consequently big ships can float on water.

These cells then send a message to the brain.

Before it reaches the earth it usually burns away.

Once it receives the information the brain figures out what you are seeing.

Word pictures

Some sentences tell the reader about an action or a happening.

The adventurer crashed through the window.

The spaceship was crushed by the octomonster.

Some just report on how things are.

The block of flats is twenty storeys high and stands in the centre of the estate.

Lara is Chloe's sister and Liam is their step-brother...

❑ Try writing three sentences on each of the following.
In each sentence just report how things are. Make a picture in words.

the classroom	where I live

❑ Try thinking of a subject and write your own sentences reporting something.

When we report on something we present a picture of it in words.

Language and instructions

Objective

Examine the grammatical conventions of instructional texts

Language issues

Procedural texts outline the steps to be taken to reach a particular end, such as the construction of a piece of furniture, the playing of a particular game or the cooking of a particular recipe. They typically prepare the reader for the activity by outlining the process to be undertaken, the items needed and any preparation: 'To make an omelette you will need...'

What typically follows is a step-by-step guide through the actions that need to be done to complete the task. The sorts of sentences this produces are ones that instruct, such as, 'Beat the eggs...', 'Shake the dice...', 'Screw the bracket into the wall...'.

The verbs in such texts will be imperative commands, such as 'Beat...' and 'Shake...', or simple second person form verbs, for example, 'You beat...', 'You shake...'. The reader is told exactly what to do and the instructions are given in order, very much reflecting the way these texts are often read as the activity described is being undertaken.

These texts also provide interesting examples of the use of prepositions, as the instructions very often direct the reader in the ways in which they should place, fit or arrange the components used in the task.

Ways of teaching

This unit should open children to the possibility that, with a grasp of what certain texts set out to do and how they can achieve these aims, children can pass judgement on the effectiveness of certain examples of procedural texts.

About the activities

Photocopiable: Imperative sentences

This activity brings children back to the particular style in which imperative sentences are written. They need to look for the sentences that are issuing an instruction directly to the reader.

Photocopiable: Writing instructions

One way of investigating the effectiveness of these instructions is for each set to be given to a different group of children for an initial attempt at the trick. The ease with which they follow them may illustrate something about the instructions. They could then swap texts and see if things become any clearer.

Photocopiable: Instruction checking

The main point to this activity is that children realize they can judge an explanatory text. They know what job it is trying to do as they can see how it matches up to the task. Children may respond with just yes/no for some of the questions, but that is fine as there is a range of texts for them to read here. Once they have done these texts they can try others (see 'Following up').

Following up

Instruction books: Children can write critical reviews of some of the instructional texts in their school library, looking at the effectiveness of the texts and how easy they are to follow. They could grade different texts according to their clarity and readability.

Pick out steps: Looking at paragraphs of text that explain a procedure, children can try counting out and finding the particular steps involved in the process described.

Imperative sentences

Imperative sentences tell the reader to do something.
For example:

❑ Cut out these sentences and sort the imperatives from the ones that are not imperatives.

Leave this room immediately.	Should I leave the room?
Once you have finished read a book.	We all sat down in a space.
Send a message saying what you plan to do.	Be quiet.
I sent a message saying what I planned to do.	How quiet are we?
Put these words in alphabetical order.	Look out of the window.
Don't make too much of a mess.	Sam looked out of the window.
We read a book once we had finished.	Is the room in a mess?
Aaron's name is first on the register.	Find a space and sit down.

Writing instructions

Sets of instructions tend to include certain types of language:

a statement of what the
instructions will help you to do

> Here is how to do the 'Seven Card Trick'

nouns saying what to use

> You will need a pack of cards

steps

> First cut the deck

❏ Look at these three texts all showing how to do the same magic trick. Look for the features listed above. Underline things you think are unclear. Decide which of the three you think is the best – and why.

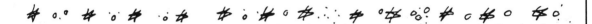

Instructions
You will need:
Paper, a pencil, a friend.

Your friend
- thinks of a number
- doubles it
- adds ten to it
- halves it
- takes away the
number first thought of.
Tell your friend the
answer is 5.

The Magic Mind-reader

- Tell your friend you are a mind-reader.
- Ask your friend to think of a number.
- They must keep it a secret.
- Tell your friend to double it.
- Then ask them to add 10 to the total.
- Now they must halve their new number.
- Whatever result they have, they must take away the number they first thought of.
- Tell them you can read their mind and the answer they now have is 5.
- It always works that way – but they will think you are a mind-reader.

Tell your friends you are a mind-reader and ask them to think of a number, double it and add 10. They then divide it by 2 and after doing that they take away the number they first though of at the start. But they still don't tell you what that number is. Now they have a new number. You tell them you know what it is and you tell them it's the number 5 and they think you are a mind-reader. Really – it is always the number 5!

Instruction checking

Here are two instruction texts.

Fruity fangs
A piece of orange peel

Frighten your family with a set of fangs that any monster would be proud of. All you need is a piece of oval-shaped orange peel large enough to fit over your teeth.
   Cut out some super fangs and pop the peel into the front of your mouth between your lips and your teeth. Now take a look in the mirror and give yourself a scare.
   Happy hauntings!

Fun with wool
Things you will need
a balloon
2 lengths of wool yarn

What you do
Lay two long pieces of wool yarn on a table and rub them lengthways with an inflated balloon. Then hold up both pieces of wool at one end and keep them about 6cm apart. What happens? Can you get the same result with string?

❑ Use them to fill in the first rows of this table.

5 = very clear   4 = clear   3 = O.K.   2 = unclear   1 = couldn't understand it!

text	is it clear what you are aiming to do?	is it clear what you will need?	are there clear steps to follow?	score out of five
Fruity Fangs				
Fun With Wool				

❑ Look at some of the books and resources around the classroom. How do they match up to this table? Give each text a score out of 5.

Discussion and persuasion

Objective
Examine the grammatical conventions of texts that persuade and discuss

Language issues
Texts that raise issues or directly appeal to the views and opinions of the reader can take two broad forms. At one extreme there are the persuasive texts that intend to win the reader over to their view, such as a campaigning leaflet or an advert. At the other end of the scale there is the discussion text that presents a balanced perspective of the issues: these are texts that give completely separate sections to people of different persuasion to put their viewpoint. Between these there are texts that allow some freedom to expound other views while hammering home their own. There are texts that pretend to present a balanced view of things while, in reality, they are giving a negative picture of one and pushing another side of the argument.

In both types of text the participants can be general: 'Bankers favour a change because…' or specific: 'Margaret Thatcher was…'. They will typically be structured in a way that links one thing to another, arguing that a new road will destroy a particular type of wildlife or that the economy is in a mess because of what this or that Government has done. The linkage and connection between things in these texts is of particular importance as is the way in which they sometimes make a direct appeal to the reader: 'So you should oppose…', 'Buy new "Zesto" and you will…'.

Ways of teaching
This unit provides an opportunity for children to find, and bring into the classroom, a range of adverts from various sources as well as discussion material from various adults.

About the activities
Photocopiable: Discussion sides
The connection between two sides of an argument is, in this photocopiable, framed in a way that should enable children to look at both sides of certain arguments. It raises the way in which the two sides are connected, using opposing words and phrases like 'however', 'but' and 'on the other hand'.

Photocopiable: Report on a discussion
The write-up of a discussion often has to collate various points of view and rephrase them in a way that makes the written summary readable. As they review this

discussion children are asked to write it up. Before undertaking the task it may be an idea to remind children of the difference between the direct and indirect reporting of speech.

Photocopiable: Persuaders
As they use this exercise to look at the language of selling and persuasion, children should be encouraged to adopt the position of a sceptic. They are going to be picking apart the adverts they look at, and noticing, in some cases, exaggerated claims. In looking at links they can try to think through the connotations conjured up by the use of a particular location or celebrity to promote a certain product. Why, for example, do certain clothes get advertised in rugged countryside, or certain drinks in rural settings?

Following up
Class discussion: The themes raised in 'Discussion sides' can form the basis for a discussion that can be taped. An edited version of the tape can be made by the teacher including the most significant comments. This edited version can form the basis for children to write up the discussion.

Teacher fallout: Children love listening to their teachers debate. If two members of staff can be roped into giving different sides of a debate children can hear and engage in a two-sided discussion.

Persuasive differences: Looking at different publications, children can survey the different persuasive texts in various contexts. What, for example do we find advertised in a comic? How is it advertised? How does this compare with the advertisements found in a television guide, or those of a broadsheet newspaper?

Discussion sides

❑ Think of something people argue about.

Some say...
Some say you shouldn't eat meat because it means animals get killed.

Discussion about meat

Some say...
Some say cars are bad for the environment.

Discussion about cars

However others say...
However others say the animals are looked after until it is time for them to be slaughtered.

However others say...
However others say people should be free to travel as they want to.

Discussions have two sides.
❑ Can you think of two topics you have heard people discussing and disagreeing about?

They could be about things in school like changes in playtime – the amount of choice you get in your activities.
They could be about things in school, or they could be about bigger issues like whether there really is a Father Christmas or whether television is bad for you.

❑ Can you fill in the speech bubbles below to show two sides of each argument.

Some say...

Some say...

However others say...

However others say...

Report on a discussion

When writing about a discussion you report the things people say:

| Politics is boring. | You can't trust what politicians say. |

either directly:

> One speaker said, "Politics is boring."
> While another added, "You can't trust what politicians say."

or indirectly.

> One speaker said politics was boring and another commented that it was hard to trust politicians.

You can collate things people said.

> It was felt that politics was boring, politicians untrustworthy.

❑ Look at these comments made in a discussion on television and write a report of the discussion on a separate sheet of paper.

It's good for children because they learn from it.

They watch too much.

There shouldn't be programmes for children on television.

They should read instead.

It keeps them quiet.

Television teaches children bad manners.

Children enjoy it – so why shouldn't they watch it?

Television can stimulate the imagination.

Children encounter so many fantastic stories on television.

Children don't know when to stop so they end up watching too much.

I don't like telly myself so don't let my children watch any.

Persuaders

Texts that persuade try to give reasons why you should do this or do that.

❑ Look at a series of adverts cut out of a magazine and complete this table. Look out for:
- adjectives used to describe the product
- the things the advert says it will do
- linking to things like famous pop stars or trendy things.

Advert	Adjectives used to describe the product	What are they saying it will do?	What are they linking it to?

Scholastic Literacy Skills
Grammar and punctuation

Investigating language

Contents of Term 3b

Unit 1: **Language contexts**	Conduct detailed language investigations Revise formal styles of writing	
Unit 2: **'Clause and effect'**	Secure understanding of complex sentences, including the effects of using clauses	
Unit 3: **Word change over time**	Conduct investigations into language change over time	
Unit 4: **Language and the media**	Investigate the use of language within the media	
Unit 5: **Language play**	Investigate idiosyncratic uses of word play	

This half-term

The various aspects of language explored in this half-term are dealt with in a way that can stimulate further investigation. Children could take up some of the issues raised and, through interviews and text gathering and analysis, they could build up their own investigation portfolio of a particular issue.

Poster notes

Investigation planner
The investigation planner provides a frame in which children and teacher can share in the planning of an investigation. They note the area they will investigate (for example, advertising) and frame their key questions (such as 'What sort of adjectives can we find in adverts?'). They should note where they will find texts and sources they should look at. They can also note people they would like to interview. Finally, they can suggest what makes the investigation worthwhile.

Sentence corners
As with the activity in Unit 2, this poster can be enlarged and written on in a shared context. The first half of an interesting sentence can be written at the top and different endings can be suggested.

Investigation planner

Investigating

Key questions

Information sources

People to talk to

Why it matters

Sentence corners

❏ In the sentence starter box write the start of a
sentence that leads up to the connective words shown.

❏ Then write seven endings to the sentence starter,
taking your cue from the connective words.

sentence starter
and
but
so
although
because
however
therefore

❏ How does the connective word in each sentence change the ending each time?

Language contexts

Objective
Conduct detailed language investigations
Revise formal styles of writing

Language issues
'Each language meets the communication needs of its speakers in an entirely adequate way, and, if these needs change, then the language changes with them.'

Trudgill (1975) p24

This idea, expressed by Trudgill, can be difficult for some people to take on board. Talk about the 'beauty of the English language' or the scientific precision of English grammar can lead to an idea that a certain form of English has some inherent goodness. The fact is, no language or dialect is inherently better than another. They adapt to fit the context in which they work. Language users adapt their usage to a context. An understanding of language opens up the potential to use it in different ways in different contexts.

Ways of teaching
In a unit in which the emphasis is upon investigating language, children can look at the use of formal language and review work they have done in earlier units. Some of the debates and discussions opened by these units may lead to longer investigations.

About the activities
Photocopiable: Use of the passive
This activity uses a range of genuine texts from various contexts given. It provides children with a chance to look at the examples but also to consider how the use of active and passive in these texts matches their own experience of similar examples. Having looked at the explanatory piece on the microscope they can consider how typical this is of explanatory sentences.

Photocopiable: Right words, right occasion
Language use reflects the context in which it is used. As they approach the various scenarios in this photocopiable children should be challenged to imagine the genuine ways in which these people would speak. The character returning the clothes may feel that he has less of a right to complain than the man with the cold food. How will the use of vocabulary and sentence type reflect the attitude of the speaker?

Photocopiable: Debate cards
This is a challenging activity to place before children at Key Stage 2 but one that many of them will relish. They have to organize their own discussion, fed by the subject matter on the cards. It is worth preparing the children beforehand by advising them that they are not out to win an argument but to explore the issues raised by the subject. As such they should realize that they should not just demolish views with which they disagree, but they should aim to think of interesting comments about the issues raised.

Following up
Conversation styles: Children can come up with a list of six diverse people they know from school or home and write their details on slips of paper. They then work in twos, each child picking up a piece of paper and trying to act out the conversation that would take place if these two people met up with each other.

Volume down: Children can watch snippets of video footage with the volume turned down. By looking at the setting and types of character they have to try to imagine what two characters could be saying to each other and the manner in which they would address one another. Some of the children might even like to try talking over the clip of film when it is replayed. The accents and mannerisms they put into the speech can create a lot of fun. Incidentally, this activity works particularly well with old black and white films.

Handle a complaint: Children can look at the process of making a complaint. They can work in pairs conducting a telephone conversation with one another in which one plays the dissatisfied customer and the other handles the complaint. Stress the need for them to use tact and to avoid insulting each other. They could review conversations to look at the sort of strategies they used and how these worked (or didn't!).

Use of the passive

❏ Look at these text extracts. Which of them are written in the passive voice? Which are written in the active voice?

extract from a newspaper article	Mr Cartwright answered, "Not guilty." The judge instructed the jury not to discuss the case outside the court. He adjourned the court until Wednesday.
extract from a diary	I went to school and met Sean at the gates. He had his arm in a sling. Said he did it ice skating.
extract from a complaint letter	We waited for an hour before the waitress brought over our pizza. We then discovered it was the wrong pizza. We then waited another hour.
extract from "Dead Meat", a short story	My Uncle Ted sent a newspaper clipping of Woody the Hood. It looked great. Woody with a big hat on his head and two mean, beady eyes staring at the camera. In handcuffs too.
extract from an adult recounting her first day at school in 1924	All the kids by now had stopped crying. We all settled down and waited for whatever there was to come. Our teacher was tall and looked like a horse, that's how she appeared to me.
extract from a conversation between two friends	"I saw Julie yesterday". "Where was she, then?" "She said she was ill but she didn't look ill to me".
extract from an encyclopedia explanation of a microscope	The focusing knob is then turned to bring the objective lens very close to the object.
extract from an advert	Our bank accounts are provided with the customer in mind. Your needs are considered, the right saving plan for you is agreed, giving you piece of mind.
headline from a newspaper	Hostages released!

❏ Write some text extracts from books in the classroom on the back of this sheet. Sort them into those that are active and those that are passive.

Right words, right occasion

Here are four different occasions. How will the people in each space speak? What is different about the way they will talk?

This man is taking a pair of trousers that were too small back to the shop. How will he talk?

This man has just been served food that is cold. How will he talk?

This girl is meeting the Prime Minister. How will she talk?

This boy is making a speech to the whole school. How will he talk?

Debate cards

❑ To investigate formal and informal language, get into groups of four, cut out the rectangles below, place them face downwards on the carpet.

❑ Take turns to pick up one rectangle. Read it to the group. The group then has to discuss it. Do they agree with the proposal or not?

Make sure that you give reasons for your opinions.

Posh people don't talk better than other people.	Children don't care about the way they talk – just so long as someone understands them.
Everybody speaks in a different way and that's a good thing.	On television, people speak differently on serious programmes.
At school they don't really teach you how to speak.	As you get older you talk better.

❑ Once you have finished write some notes about what people said.

'Clause and effect'

Objective
Secure understanding of complex sentences, including the effects of using clauses

Language issues
There is a classic piece of comedy writing used in many scripts that shows how effective the use of a particular connective can be. The speaker is lauding praise along the lines of:
'I think of Tom and I would like to say how generous, charming, intelligent, compassionate and brilliant he is...'. This lengthy clause ends with the word '...but...' and the speaker proceeds to explain why he *cannot* say the above!

Clauses can be strung together to have varied effects and this can, to a large extent, depend upon the connecting word or phrase.

Ways of teaching
In this unit the emphasis is upon investigation into language. Children are investigating the way in which clause structure gives the language the potential to turn, mid-sentence, in various directions. As such the emphasis should be upon moving beyond learning that this can happen to look at the actual effects that this can have within a sentence.

About the activities
Photocopiable: Sentences turn corners
The essential feature of the incomplete sentences in this activity is the way in which they are affected by the connecting word. Children should be brought back to their completed results to compare the various second halves they added and see how these matched up the start of the sentence. The 'Sentence corners' poster can be used to explain and extend this activity.

Photocopiable: Multi clauses
The rebuilding of these sentences can take time. As they endeavour to find sensible options children will inevitably create some odd examples that they may want to note down, such as 'Our cat ran up the tree because it was the first day of the holidays until the sun came out and it evaporated'. In this activity, as with the previous one, the connecting words provide interesting material to look at. How do they affect the way these sentences turn out?

Photocopiable: Investigating clauses
As children find the sections of the books they are looking at in this activity there needs to be some system to ensure that they are drawing upon genuinely random samples. They could, for example, take three sentences from the middle of page 5 in each of the texts they are surveying. Whatever system is hatched, the teacher needs to avoid sentence rigging!

Following up
Gobbledegook: Looking at a range of texts, children can evaluate them to see which they think is the simplest. They could look at the use of clauses and investigate whether these make sentences harder to follow. They can try to find an example of a text that is hard to follow.

Simplify: Children can look at a text with complex sentences and think how they would simplify it. Could they turn each clause into a simple sentence of its own? They could try and imagine that they are writing the text out for a younger audience.

Clause relations: Children could try to think of clauses in sentences as being characters. They could look at how each clause relates to the other(s) and ask themselves whether they agree or disagree with each other. This could follow on from the 'Sentences turn corners' activity, in which the second clauses relate in different ways to the first clauses.

Sentences turn corners

❑ Look at the sentence starters below. The same starter is followed by three spaces in which three different endings could be written. Look at the connecting word. This could change the ending you write.

Sentence starters	Connectives	
I would love to help you	and	
I would love to help you	but	
I would love to help you	so	
My school is great	although	
My school is great	and also	
My school is great	because	
It's a beautiful day	however	
It's a beautiful day	therefore	
It's a beautiful day	and	
We have got homework	and	
We have got homework	so	
We have got homework	however	

❑ What sorts of difference did the connecting words make?

Multi clauses

The strips below show some mixed up sentences. Clauses have been separated from clauses. Can you try to make sense of them? Write them out on a separate sheet of paper.

My Uncle couldn't breathe
There was a puddle outside our front door
Mum planned a picnic
when it was his fortieth birthday
however his drill wasn't working
when next door's dog barked at him
until the sun came out and it evaporated.
so we all made a card for him.
but it rained all day.

because my little brother was sitting on him
Our cat ran up the tree
so instead he joined us for a game of football.
after it rained heavily
because it was the first day of the holidays
so he shouted, "Get off."
Our teacher organized a party
and Mum had to climb up to get it down.
The caretaker came to mend our window

❏ What words helped you to link the different pieces together?

Investigating clauses

This is an investigation into the complexity of sentences within books.

❑ Collect a pile of different books from the school library.

❑ Look at the sentences in these texts. Select three sample sentences from the middle of the book. Count the number of clauses in each sample. Make a note of one of the sentences.

Text title	What sort of book is it?	Number of clauses in sample sentence	Example sentence

❑ Once you have filled in the sections cut them out. Stick them onto a separate sheet with the most complex text at the top and the least complex at the bottom.

Word change over time

Objective
Conduct investigations into language change over time

Language issues
There are a number of reasons for the changes in the meaning and function of words over time. Words can be created in various ways, such as when common things such as a 'Sandwich' or a 'Boycott' are named after their originators. Words can be adopted from one language into another, such as the word 'slogan' from Gaelic and 'potato' from Taino, an extinct Caribbean language. Words can also be altered through the addition of prefixes and suffixes. Shakespeare made a habit of adding prefixes such as 'un-' and 'en-' to words and, in doing so, added the following to English: endanger, enthral, entomb. This word creation was, in his case, for dramatic effect.

Words can also alter their meaning over time: a word like 'nice' once meant 'simple' and has its origins in the Latin word 'nescius' meaning 'ignorant'.

Language is constantly changing over time and there are regularly stories in the press about supplements adding a new set of words to one of the classic dictionaries.

Ways of teaching
The emphasis in this unit is upon children looking at this language change as it happens. They can look at new words and their meanings and review the whole idea of change over time. It also introduces children to an investigation of old forms of English. While this is, in some ways, a word-based activity and therefore not obviously a part of grammar and punctuation, this unit focuses upon phrases and the use of words in a context that enables the reader to decode the obscurities of the language.

About the activities
Photocopiable: Chaucer's words
One way of approaching this is to have the children look at the text without the glossary before they attempt to figure out the passage with its assistance. Then they can read the text and use the glossary. The children should pencil the modern equivalents that they need above the original words. There are some they may not need, such as 'Aprille'. Once this is done they can try to read and make sense of the whole passage.

Photocopiable: Word origins
The focus in this activity is upon the way language develops over time. As such it shouldn't be treated as a matching game; rather, children should be urged to try to see the link between the original word and the modern word. Words are borrowed in a way that often changes their meaning interestingly. As such, the links are there even if they are sometimes hard to guess.

Photocopiable: King James language
Certain events like Caxton's printing and the birth of broadcasting have had immeasurable effects on English. This activity brings children into contact with one of those significant events in the history of the language, the production of the King James Bible. Children can try to figure out these idiomatic expressions for themselves but the investigative element will involve them taking the expressions to other adults and asking how they would use these phrases. They could also see if the adults concerned know the origin of these expressions.

Following up
New words: Children could try thinking of words that are entering the English language. The recent history of English has seen the addition of 'Internet', 'video' and 'road rage'. Can they think of other expressions that are currently coming into use? They may have examples of playground slang, such as the use of the word 'chinny' for 'liar' or 'bad' being used to mean 'good'.

Bluff words: Old and obscure words can be found and children can be asked to guess the meaning of the word from three possible alternatives. One interesting slant on this is to ask children to think of the alternatives. Faced with a word like 'hyperbole' children will listen to it and think what it sounds like, which may lead to some interesting definitions of the word as 'an air pump' or 'a huge balloon'.

Named after us: Many names, such as Sandwich and 'Boycott' have become words in common use. Children can imagine that their names will become common nouns or verbs. What thing or action would they want their word describe? What would people mean by the verb 'to thomas'?

Chaucer's words

Chaucer wrote *The Canterbury Tales* in the 14th century. In this introductory piece he talks about the time of year when people like to go on pilgrimages. A pilgrimage is a journey to religious places.

Whan that Aprille with his shoures sote

The droghte of Marche hath perced to the rote,

And bathed every veyen in swich licour,

Of which vertue engendered is the flour;

...Than longen folk to goon on pilgrimages.

Chaucer wrote in Middle English. This was an old variety of English.

❑ Using the glossary below can you work out what Chaucer was saying?

Aprille	April	*perced*	pierced, covered or touched
droghte	drought, lack of rain	*pilgrimages*	pilgrimages
engendered	made, caused to exist	*rote*	root
flour	flower	*shoures*	showers, as in rain showers
folk	people	*sote*	sweet
goon	go	*swich*	such
hath	has	*than*	then
licour	drink	*vertue*	virtue
longen	want, as in longing	*veyen*	vein
Marche	March	*whan*	when

Word origins

Many of the words in the English language are borrowed from other languages.

rein	from Latin **retinere** (meaning "hold back")

Sometimes you can still see links between words and their origins.

❑ Look at these words:

buckle	science	hollow	tale	ball

atom	none	able	straight	diet

❑ Now look at these words from other languages. Can you see the ancestors of the English words? Write the English word in the correct space. Can you suggest a link between the words?

Old word	Modern English word	Link
Latin **habilus** (active)		
Latin **ballare** (to dance)		
French **boucle** (ring)		
Latin **scient** (from) **scire** (know)		
Anglo Saxon **strechan** (stretch)		
Greek **diata** (manner of living)		
Greek **atomos** (cannot be divided)		
Anglo Saxon **ne** (not) **an** (one)		
Anglo Saxon **hol** (hole)		
Anglo Saxon **tellan** (to tell)		

King James language

An idiom is a sequence of words used together. They are usually images that describe something in an interesting way. For example, when people say "in my mind's eye" they don't mean in an eye inside their head, they mean in their imagination the way the mind sees things.
In 1611 the King James Version of the Bible was published. 54 people translated old Greek and Hebrew texts into English.

Ἐὰν ταῖς γλώσσαις τῶν ἀνθρώπων λαλῶ καὶ τῶν ἀγγέλων,

In their translation they used some phrases that have become idioms. Here are some. Can you guess what they mean and then ask adults what they think the idiom means? They are common phrases. How many have you heard of before?

idioms	it could mean	adults' opinions
my brother's keeper *Genesis 4*		
the apple of his eye *Deuteronomy 32*		
a man after his own heart *1 Samuel 13*		
the skin of my teeth *Job 19*		
go from strength to strength *Psalms 84*		
at their wits' end *Psalms 107*		
the straight and narrow *Matthew 7*		
the twinkling of an eye *1 Corinthians 15*		

Language and the media

Objective
Investigate the use of language within the media

Language issues
One area of society that offers a rich resource of specialized and rarefied language use is the mass media. The media provide an opportunity to look at how language has been developed and expanded by the purposes for which it is used. In newspaper journalism there are particular terms used to describe the 'headline' and the 'standfirst' (the little piece of text that stands between some headlines and some stories). Film offers a range of technical terms, such as 'shot' as well as critical terminology and labels of different genres. The term 'semantic field' is applied to a set of terms that tend to be associated with a particular topic; the language of weather, for example, includes words like 'front', 'low pressure', 'gale' within its semantic field. In looking at the language of media it can be seen that various sectors of this broad area, such as television and advertising, have their own semantic field. Within these sectors there are fields associated with what is being communicated through the media; politics uses terms like 'spin doctor', 'lobby' and 'on the record', whereas sports commentary, pop music and so on all have fields of their own.

Ways of teaching
This unit brings the use of English into a setting in which it is flourishing. Children should be given this opportunity to celebrate the way in which the media use the language in so many varied ways. It is also a unit that should spark off a fair bit of investigation at home, as children apply the ideas presented in the photocopiables to their after school viewing.

About the activities
Photocopiable: Media word type
The key to making this activity work is to select good portions of television to watch. Obscure and clearly defined pieces, such as the way the financial markets are reported or the pre-race discussion of horses can provide the sort of snippet. They don't need to be long. The brief introduction to a pop song can provide as much material as an extended chunk of general waffle.

Photocopiable: The language of adverts
Persuasion is the name of the game in this activity. Children need to adopt a bit of healthy scepticism hunting out the words and phrases that are aiming at hooking

the viewer into spending money. They also need to try to keep within a particular set of adverts, such as car adverts. By doing this they can find some interesting common themes, sometimes indicating a trend in advertising. To take cars as an example, there has been a shift from emphasizing the speed of cars to promoting their safety features. This is the sort of trend children may find as they collate common terminology.

Photocopiable: Technical vocabulary
One facet of language this activity should bring home to children is the technical nature of terminology in a particular field. It is worth getting children to try and learn the terminology, possibly setting a quiz to see who can remember the most terms. They then have them to hand as they watch a snippet of film, without having to refer to the sheet.

Following up
Advertise: Collecting the words they have seen used to advertise a particular product, children can try to devise their own advert. They should stick with a product they have surveyed and try using some of the vocabulary they have collected as well as adding their own word choices.

Using the vocabulary: Drawing on the technical vocabulary listed in the 'Technical vocabulary' photocopiable, children can try devising their own storyboard. This is a set of rectangles that chart how they would film a particular scene. They could use a scene from a novel or one of their own devising.

Specialists: Children might want to follow this unit up with an investigation of the level of technical terminology in other fields. They could interview the school nurse or contact a representative of a local business and ask them for some examples of the sort of technical vocabulary they have to use.

Media word type

❑ Watch some distinctive bits of television such as:

a weather forecast   a sports report   an advert   a presenter talking to younger children

Well, Brian, I gently tapped the ball past their defence and dribbled it into an open goal.

Look out for words that are special to that type of programme!

❑ Try to watch the same sort of thing more than once. Make a note of some of the nouns, verbs, adjectives and adverbs you hear.

❑ Note them on the chart below.

Type of extract	Nouns	Verbs	Adjectives	Adverbs

The language of adverts

Adverts contain sentences that describe their products. They try to persuade you to buy them.

It's scrummy and yummy and delicious!

The smoothest and safest!

Clean, fresh and biologically formulated to get to the toughest stains!

❑ Look at a selection of adverts cut out from a newspaper. Try to find adverts for the same sort of product.

cars

furniture

films

shop sales

❑ Try to find some sentences with lots of adjectives.

Advert for	Adjectives

Technical vocabulary

Here are some technical nouns used by people who make films.

Try learning what they mean and then watching a bit of a film. See if you can point out some of these techniques in the clip you watch.

shot	one continuous bit of film
cut	a break between two shots
long shot	a shot that shows a lot, such as a person or people and all the surroundings
close-up	a picture which shows a fairly small part of the scene, such as a face
point of view shot	a shot that films things as a character in the film would see them
dialogue	characters speaking to each other
zoom	the camera zooms in from a long shot, getting closer and closer
pan	the camera swivels to follow something or someone
special effect	a made up effect, like a spaceship or a moving dragon
external	a scene set outside
internal	a scene set indoors
voice over	a voice telling something about the story, speaking over the things we see on the screen

Language play

Objective
Investigate idiosyncratic uses of word play

Language issues
One of the key features of language that can be investigated is the way in which it is so open to play. Linguists have written entire books on the subject of the way in which people have played with language over the years. The term 'play' is not used in a frivolous sense. When Dylan Thomas speaks of something as grim as death in the words 'Do not go gentle into that good night' he is, in a sense, playing around with the meaning of words in order to conjure up an image. Linguists refer to this as deviation, a conscious deviation from the norms of language.

At the other end of the scale we have the question and answer joke that can play upon the potential for words to mean more than one thing. Between these two there is a vast range of language play – long may it remain so!

Ways of teaching
This unit asks children to investigate the whole area of language play. The obvious way for them to do this is for them to play with language themselves. However, in doing this they should try and look at what it is about language that makes it something we can manipulate and enjoy in this way.

About the activities
Photocopiable: Things they say
One of the best ways into this activity is for children to think of the predictable sayings owned by various television personalities. Sometimes there are certain call and response exchanges between a quiz presenter and the audience; on other occasions it could just be the phrase a magician or comedian uses to pepper their act. However, they should try and bring the activity closer to home. Teachers have their catchphrases too!

Photocopiable: Proverbs
Proverbs wrap significant messages up in interesting images. Children should try to visualize the proverbs in this activity as a way of figuring out what they are communicating.

Once the children have figured out the message of the proverbs featured in the activity they could try to invent their own.

Photocopiable: Joke sentences
A collection of the saddest and oldest jokes – fit only for investigation. However, by looking at these jokes children can focus upon the double meanings and various uses of the words on which the joke hinges. In some cases this involves the change of grammatical word class (such as the use of 'cross' as an adjective in 'crossroad'). Children need to make notes around the edge picking out how the joke works.

Following up
Illustrate proverbs: Proverbs conjure up some incredible images. Children can try to illustrate the proverbs they have investigated, depicting cooks and glass houses.

Joke book: Children might be able to use some of the techniques they have found in the jokes they investigate to devise their own jokes. One particular feature to exploit is the double meaning of words.

Things they say

Some people say the same words again and again. These become known as catchphrases.

 If I have to tell you again...

 Hello, Good morning and welcome.

 Let's see your score and score some more.

 Elementary, my dear Watson.

Can you think of some people (real or not)?
❑ Draw their face and write their catchphrase.

_____ always says:	_____ always says:
_____ always says:	_____ always says:

Proverbs

Proverbs are old phrases that carry a meaning.

Proverb	Means
A stitch in time saves nine.	If you do a job when it needs doing it will save you having to do a bigger job later on.

Like when a stitch comes loose – if you sew it straight away it will save you having to mend nine more when they unravel.

Cut out the rectangles below. Stick them down on a separate sheet of paper, matching proverbs to meaning.

❑ Can you explain the proverbs?

Proverb	Meanings
All work and no play makes Jack a dull boy.	Too many people trying to do a job make a mess of it.
Too many cooks spoil the broth.	People with faults in themselves shouldn't pick out faults in others.
Every cloud has a silver lining.	You need to have a rest from work else you don't work so well.
The early bird always catches the worm.	If you get to something early you get the best of it.
People who live in glass houses shouldn't throw stones.	Check before you go ahead with a venture.
No use crying over spilt milk.	When a bad thing has happened it has happened and that's that!
Once bitten, twice shy.	Something good can come out of bad things that happen.
Look before you leap.	If you have a bad experience with something you are more careful next time.

Joke sentences

Many jokes use features of language.

❑ Look at this one: Why do leopards never escape from the zoo?
They are always spotted.

Here are some points about it.   Why do leopards never escape from the zoo?
They are always spotted.

'spotted' can be an
adjective or a verb

this can mean 'spotted' like in
spots or 'spotted' like in seen

❑ Try pointing out how the language of these jokes works.

Who invented fire? *Some bright spark.*	Why did the boy take a pencil to bed? *To draw the curtains.*	Why doesn't the sea spill off the earth? *Because it is tide.*
Sam: My dog has got no nose. Joe: How does he smell? Sam: Terrible.	Sam: Do you want to hear a secret about butter? Joe: Yes. Sam: O.K. - but promise not to spread it.	Which band has no instruments? *An elastic band.*

Subject knowledge

1: Preliminary notes about grammar

Grammar involves the way in which words of different types are combined into sentences. The explanatory sections that follow will include definitions of types of word along with notes on how they are combined into sentences.

Three preliminary points about grammar:

❏ Function is all-important. Where a word is placed in relation to another word is crucial in deciding whether it is functioning as a verb or a noun. For example, the word 'run' will often be thought of as a verb. However, in a sentence like 'They went for a run', the word functions as a noun and the verb is 'went'.

❏ There are some consistencies in the way spelling is linked to grammar. For example, words like 'play' and 'shout' have the '-ed' ending to make past tense verbs, 'played' and 'shouted'. Adjectives like 'quick' and 'slow' take a '-ly' ending to make adverbs like 'quickly' and 'slowly'. There are exceptions to these rules but such consistencies can still prove useful when it comes to understanding the grammar of sentences.

❏ Nothing is sacred in language. Rules change over time, the double negative has gained currency and regional variation in accent and dialect is now far more valued than has been the case in the past. The rules of grammar that follow are subject to change as the language we use lives and grows.

2: Words and functions

Grammar picks out the functions of words. The major classes or types of word in the English language are:

noun

The name of something or someone, including concrete things, such as 'dog' or 'tree', and abstract things, such as 'happiness' or 'fear'.

pronoun

A word that replaces a noun. The noun 'John' in 'John is ill' can be replaced by a pronoun 'he', making 'He is ill'.

verb

A word that denotes an action or a happening. In the sentence 'I ate the cake' the verb is 'ate'. These are sometimes referred to as 'doing' words.

adjective

A word that modifies a noun. In the phrase 'the little boat' the adjective 'little' describes the noun 'boat'.

adverb

A word that modifies a verb. In the phrase 'he slowly walked' the adverb is 'slowly'.

preposition

A word or phrase that shows the relationship of one thing to another. In the phrase 'the house beside the sea' the preposition 'beside' places the two nouns in relation to each other.

conjunction

A word or phrase that joins other words and phrases. A simple example is the word 'and' that joins nouns in 'Snow White and Doc and Sneezy'.

article

The indefinite articles in English are 'a' and 'an' and the definite article is 'the'. Articles appear before nouns and denote whether the noun is specific ('give me the book') or not ('give me a book').

interjection

A word or phrase expressing or exclaiming an emotion, such as 'Oh!' and 'Aaargh!'

The various word types can be found in the following example sentences:

Lou	saw	his	new	house	from	the	train.
noun	verb	pronoun	adjective	noun	preposition	article	noun
Yeow!	I	hit	my	head	on	the	door.
interjection	pronoun	verb	pronoun	noun	preposition	article	noun
Amir	sadly	lost	his	bus fare	down	the	drain.
noun	adverb	verb	pronoun	noun	preposition	article	noun
Give	Jan	a	good	book	for	her	birthday.
verb	noun	article	adjective	noun	conjunction	pronoun	noun

The pages that follow provide more information on these word classes.

Nouns

There are four types of noun in English.

Common nouns are general names for things. For example, in the sentence 'I fed the dog', the noun 'dog' could be used to refer to any dog, not to a specific one. Other examples include 'boy', 'country', 'book', 'apple'.

Proper nouns are the specific names given to identify things or people. In a phrase like 'Sam is my dog' the word 'dog' is the common noun but 'Sam' is a proper noun because it refers to and identifies a specific dog. Other examples include 'the Prime Minister', 'Wales' and 'Amazing Grace'.

Collective nouns refer to a group of things together, such as 'a flock (of sheep)' or 'a bunch (of bananas)'.

A **noun** is the name of someone or something.

Abstract nouns refer to things that are not concrete, such as an action, a concept, an event, quality or state. Abstract nouns like 'happiness' and 'fulfilment' refer to ideas or feelings which are uncountable; others, such as 'hour', 'joke' and 'quantity' are countable.

Nouns can be singular or plural. To change a singular to a plural the usual rule is to add 's'. This table includes other rules to bear in mind, however:

If the singular ends in:	Rule	Examples
'y' after a consonant	Remove 'y', add 'ies'	party ➜ parties
'y' after a vowel	add 's'	donkey ➜ donkeys
'o' after a consonant	add 'es'	potato ➜ potatoes
'o' after a vowel	add 's'	video ➜ videos
a sound like 's', such as 's', 'sh', 'tch', 'x', 'z'	add 'es'	kiss ➜ kisses dish ➜ dishes watch ➜ watches
'ch' sounding like it does at the end of 'perch'	add 'es'	church ➜ churches

Pronouns

A **pronoun** is a word that stands in for a noun.

There are different classes of pronoun. The main types are:

Personal pronouns, referring to people or things, such as 'I', 'you', 'it'. The personal pronouns distinguish between subject and object case (I/me, he/him, she/her, we/us, they/them and the archaic thou/thee).

Reflexive pronouns, referring to people or things that are also the subject of the sentence. In the sentence 'You can do this yourself' the pronoun 'yourself' refers to 'you'. Such pronouns end with '-self' or '-selves'. Other examples include 'myself', 'themselves'.

Possessive pronouns identify people or things as belonging to a person or thing. For example, in the sentence 'The book is hers' the possessive pronoun 'hers' refers to 'the book'. Other examples include 'its' and 'yours'. Note that possessive pronouns never take an apostrophe.

Relative pronouns link relative clauses to their nouns. In the sentence 'The man who was in disguise sneaked into the room' the relative clause 'who was in disguise' provides extra information about 'the man'. This relative clause is linked by the relative pronoun 'who'. Other examples include 'whom', 'which' and 'that'.

Interrogative pronouns are used in questions. They refer to the thing that is being asked about. In the question 'What is your name?' and 'Where is the book?' the pronouns 'what' and 'where' stand for the answers – the name and the location of the book.

Demonstrative pronouns are pronouns that 'point'. They are used to show the relation of the speaker to an object. There are four demonstrative pronouns in English: 'this', 'that', 'these', 'those', used as in 'This is my house' and 'That is your house'. They have specific uses, depending upon the position of the object to the speaker:

	Near to speaker	Far away from speaker
Singular	this	that
Plural	these	those

Indefinite pronouns stand in for an indefinite noun. The indefinite element can be the number of elements or the nature of them but they are summed up in ambiguous pronouns such as 'any', 'some' or 'several'. Other examples are the pronouns that end with '-body', '-one' and '-thing', such as 'somebody', 'everyone' and 'anything'.

Person

Personal, reflexive and possessive pronouns can be in the first, second or third person.

First person pronouns (I, we) involve the speaker or writer.

Second person pronouns (you) refer to the listener or reader.

Third person pronouns refer to something other than these two participants in the communication (he, she, it, they).

The person of the pronoun will agree with particular forms of verbs: I like/ She likes.

Verbs

The **tense** of a verb places a happening in time. The main three tenses are the present, past and future.

A **verb** is a word that denotes an action or a happening.

To express an action that will take place in the future, verbs appear with 'will' or 'shall' (or 'going to'). The regular past tense is formed by the addition of the suffix '-ed', although some of the most common verbs in English (the 'strong' verbs) have irregular past tenses.

Present tense (happening now)	Past tense (happened in past)	Future tense (to happen in future)
am, say, find, kick	was, said, found, kicked	will be, will say, shall find, shall kick

Continuous verbs

The present participle form of a verb is used to show a continuous action. Whereas a past tense like 'kicked' denotes an action that happened ('I kicked'), the present participle denotes the action as happening and continuing as it is described ('I was kicking', the imperfect tense, or 'I am kicking', the present continuous). There is a sense in these uses of an action that has not ended.

The present participle usually ends in '-ing', such as 'walking', 'finding', and continuous verbs are made with a form of the verb 'be', such as 'was' or 'am': 'I was running' and 'I am running'.

Auxiliary verbs

Auxiliary verbs 'help' other verbs – they regularly accompany full verbs, always preceding them in a verb phrase. The auxiliary verbs in English can be divided into three categories:

Primary verbs are used to indicate the timing of a verb, such as 'be', 'have' or 'did' (including all their variations such as 'was', 'were', 'has', 'had' and so on). These can be seen at work in verb forms like 'I was watching a film', 'He has finished eating', 'I didn't lose my keys'.

Modal verbs indicate the possibility of an action occurring or the necessity of it happening, such as 'I might watch a film', 'I should finish eating' and 'I shouldn't lose my keys'. The modal verbs in English are: would, could, might, should, can, will, shall, may, and must. These verbs never function on their own as main verbs. They always act as auxiliaries helping other verbs.

Marginal modals, namely 'dare', 'need', 'ought to' and 'used to'. These act as modals, such as in the sentences 'I dared enter the room', 'You need to go away' and 'I ought to eat my dinner', but they can also act as main verbs, as in 'I need cake'.

Adjectives

An **adjective** is a word that modifies a noun.

The main function of adjectives is to define quality or quantity. Examples of the use of descriptions of quality include: 'good story', 'sad day' and 'stupid dog'. Examples of the use of descriptions of quantity include 'some stories', 'ten days' and 'many dogs'.

Adjectives can appear in one of three different degrees of intensity. In the table below it can be seen that there are '-er' and '-est' endings that show an adjective is comparative or superlative, though, as can be seen, there are exceptions. The regular comparative is formed by the addition of the suffix '-er' to shorter words and 'more' to longer words (kind/kinder, beautiful/more beautiful). The regular superlative is formed by the addition of the suffix '-est' to shorter words and 'most' to longer words. Note, however, that some common adjectives have irregular comparatives and superlatives.

Nominative	Comparative	Superlative
The nominative is the plain form that describes a noun.	The comparative implies a comparison between the noun and something else.	The superlative is the ultimate degree of a particular quality.
Examples	**Examples**	**Examples**
long	longer	longest
small	smaller	smallest
big	bigger	biggest
fast	faster	fastest
bad	worse	worst
good	better	best
far	farther/further	farthest/furthest

Adverbs

Adverbs provide extra information about the time, place or manner in which a verb happened.

Manner Provides information about the manner in which the action was done.	Ali *quickly* ran home. The cat climbed *fearfully* up the tree.
Time Provides information about the time at which the action occurred.	*Yesterday* Ali ran home. *Sometimes* the cat climbed up the tree.
Place Provides information about where the action took place.	*Outside* Ali ran home. *In the garden* the cat climbed up the tree.

An **adverb** is a word that modifies a verb.

Variations in the degree of intensity of an adverb are indicated by other adjectives such as 'very', 'rather', 'quite' and 'somewhat'. Comparative forms include 'very quickly', 'rather slowly', and 'most happily'.

The majority of single-word adverbs are made by adding '-ly' to an adjective: 'quick/quickly', 'slow/slowly' and so on.

Prepositions

Prepositions show how nouns or pronouns are positioned in relation to other nouns and pronouns in the same sentence. This can often be the location of one thing in relation to another in space, such as 'on', 'over', 'near'; or time, such as 'before', 'after'.

Prepositions are usually placed before a noun. They can consist of one word ('The cat *in* the tree...'), two words ('The cat *close to* the gate...') or three ('The cat *on top of* the roof...').

A **preposition** is a word or phrase that shows the relationship of one thing to another.

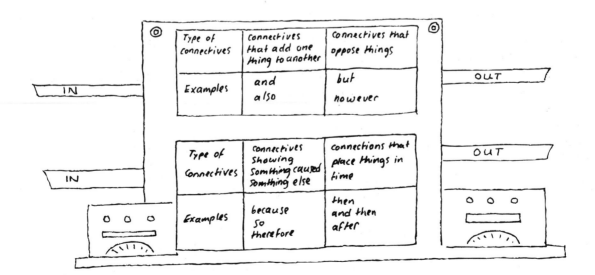

Conjunctions

Conjunctions can join words or clauses in one of four ways:

Name of conjunction	Nature of conjunction	Examples
Addition	One or more things together	We had our tea *and* went out to play. It was a cold day – *also* it rained.
Opposition	One or more things in opposition	I like coffee *but* my brother hates it. It could rain *or* it could snow.
Time	One or more things connected over time	Toby had his tea *then* went out to play. The bus left *before* we reached the stop.
Cause	One or more things causing or caused by another	I took a map *so that* we wouldn't get lost. We got lost *because* we had the wrong map.

A **conjunction** is a word or phrase that joins other words and phrases.

3: Understanding sentences

Types of sentence

The four main types of sentence are **declarative**, **interrogative**, **imperative** and **exclamatory**. The function of a sentence has an effect on the word order; imperatives, for example, often begin with a verb.

Sentence type	Function	Examples
Declarative	Makes a statement	The house is down the lane. Joe rode the bike.
Interrogative	Asks a question	Where is the house? What is Joe doing?
Imperative	Issues a command or direction	Turn left at the traffic lights. Get on your bike!
Exclamatory	Issues an interjection	Wow, what a mess! Oh no!

Sentences: Clauses and complexities

Phrases

A phrase is a set of words performing a grammatical function. In the sentence 'The little, old, fierce dog brutally chased the sad and fearful cat', there are three distinct units performing grammatical functions. The first phrase in this sentence essentially names the dog and provides descriptive information. This is a noun phrase, performing the job of a noun – 'the little, old, fierce dog'. To do this the phrase uses adjectives. The important thing to look out for is the way in which words build around a key word in a phrase. So here the words 'little', 'old' and 'fierce' are built around the word 'dog'. In examples like these, 'dog' is referred to as the **headword** and the adjectives are termed **modifiers**. Together, the modifier and headword make up the noun phrase. Modifiers can also come after the noun, as in 'The little, old, fierce dog that didn't like cats brutally chased the sad and fearful cat'. In this example 'little, 'old' and 'fierce' are **premodifiers** and the phrase 'that didn't like cats' is a **postmodifier**.

The noun phrase is just one of the types of phrase that can be made.

Phrase type	Examples
Noun phrase	The *little, old fierce dog* didn't like cats. She gave him *a carefully and colourfully covered book*.
Verb phrase	The dog *had been hiding* in the house. The man *climbed through* the window without a sound.
Adjectival phrase	The floor was *completely clean*. The floor was *so clean you could eat your dinner off it*.
Adverbial phrase	I finished my lunch *very slowly indeed*. *More confidently than usual*, she entered the room.
Prepositional phrase	The cat sat *at the top of* the tree. The phone rang *in the middle of* the night.

Notice that phrases can appear within phrases. A noun phrase like 'carefully and colourfully covered book' contains the adjectival phrase 'carefully and colourfully covered'. This string of words forms the adjectival phrase in which the words 'carefully' and 'colourfully' modify the adjective 'covered'. Together these words 'carefully and colourfully covered' modify the noun 'book', creating a distinct noun phrase. This is worth noting as it shows how the boundaries between phrases can be blurred, a fact that can cause confusion unless borne in mind!

Clauses

Clauses are units of meaning included within a sentence, usually containing a verb and other elements linked to it. 'The burglar ran' is a clause containing the definite article, noun and verb; 'The burglar quickly ran from the little house' is also a clause that adds an adverb, preposition and adjective. The essential element in a clause is the verb. Clauses look very much like small sentences, indeed sentences can be constructed of just one clause: 'The burglar hid', 'I like cake'.

Sentences can also be constructed out of a number of clauses linked together: 'The burglar ran and I chased him because he stole my cake.' This sentence contains three clauses: 'The burglar ran', 'I chased him', 'he stole my cake'.

Clauses and phrases: the difference

Clauses include participants in an action denoted by a verb. Phrases, however, need not necessarily contain a verb. These phrases make little sense on their own: 'without a sound', 'very slowly indeed'. They work as part of a clause.

Simple, compound and complex sentences

The addition of clauses can make complex or compound sentences.

Simple sentences are made up of one clause, for example: 'The dog barked', 'Sam was scared'.

Compound sentences are made up of clauses added to clauses. In compound sentences each of the clauses is of equal value; no clause is dependent on another. An example of a compound sentence is: 'The dog barked and the parrot squawked'. Both these clauses are of equal importance: 'The dog barked', 'the parrot squawked'.

Other compound sentences include, for example: 'I like coffee and I like chocolate', 'I like coffee, but I don't like tea'.

Complex sentences are made up of a main clause with a subordinate clause or clauses. Subordinate clauses make sense in relation to the main clause. They say something about it and are dependent upon it, for example in the sentences: 'The dog barked because he saw a burglar', 'Sam was scared so he phoned the police'.

In both these cases the subordinate clause ('he saw a burglar', 'he phoned the police') is elaborating on the main clause. They explain why the dog barked or why Sam was scared and, in doing so, are subordinate to those actions. The reader needs to see the main clauses to fully appreciate what the subordinate ones are stating.

Subject and object

The **subject** of a sentence or clause is the agent that performs the action denoted by the verb – '*Shaun* threw the ball'. The **object** is the agent to which the verb is done – 'ball'. It could be said that the subject does the verb to the object (a simplification but a useful one). The simplest type of sentence is known as the SVO (subject–verb–object) sentence (or clause), as in 'You lost your way', 'I found the book' and 'Lewis met Chloe'.

The active voice and the passive voice

These contrast two ways of saying the same thing:

Active voice	Passive voice
I found the book.	The book was found by me.
Megan met Ben.	Ben was met by Megan.
The cow jumped over the moon.	The moon was jumped over by the cow.

The two types of clause put the same subject matter in a different **voice**. Passive clauses are made up of a subject and verb followed by an agent.

The book	was found by	me.
subject	verb	agent
Ben	was met by	Megan.
subject	verb	agent

Sentences can be written in the active or the passive voice. A sentence can be changed from the active to the passive voice by:
- ❏ moving the subject to the end of the clause
- ❏ moving the object to the start of the clause
- ❏ changing the verb or verb phrase by placing a form of the verb 'be' before it (as in 'was found')
- ❏ changing the verb or verb phrase by placing 'by' after it.
  In passive clauses the agent can be deleted, either because it does not need mentioning or because a positive choice is made to omit it. Texts on science may leave out the agent, with sentences such as 'The water is added to the salt and stirred'.

4: Punctuation

Punctuation provides marks within sentences that guide the reader. Speech doesn't need punctuation (and would sound bizarre if it included noises for full stops etc). In speech, much is communicated by pausing, changing tone and so on. In writing, the marks within and around a sentence provide indications of when to pause, when something is being quoted and so on.

Punctuation mark	Uses	Examples
A	**Capital letter** 1. Start a sentence. 2. Indicate proper nouns. 3. Emphasize certain words.	All I want is cake. You can call me Al. I want it TOMORROW!
.	**Full stop** Ends sentences that are not questions or exclamations.	This is a sentence.
?	**Question mark** Ends a sentence that is a question.	Is this a question?
!	**Exclamation mark** Ends a sentence that is an exclamation.	Don't do that!
" " **' '**	**Quotation (speech) marks (or inverted commas)** Enclose direct speech. Can be double or single.	"Help me," the man yelled. 'Help me,' the man yelled.
,	**Comma** 1. Places a pause between clauses within a sentence. 2. Separates items in a list. 3. Separates adjectives in a series. 4. Completely encloses clauses inserted in a sentence. 5. Marks speech from words denoting who said them.	We were late, although it didn't matter. You will need eggs, butter, salt and flour. I wore a long, green, frilly skirt. We were, after we had rushed to get there, late for the film. 'Thank you,' I said.
–	**Hyphen** Connects elements of certain words.	Co-ordinator, south-west.
:	**Colon** 1. Introduces lists (including examples).	To go skiing these are the main items you will need: a warm hat, goggles and sunscreen.

continued...

Punctuation mark	Uses	Examples
	2. Introduces summaries. 3. Introduces (direct) quotations. 4. Introduces a second clause that expands or illustrates the meaning of the first.	We have learned the following on the ski slope: do a snow plough to slow down… My instructor always says: 'Bend those knees.' The snow hardened: it turned into ice.
;	**Semicolon** 1. Separates two closely linked clauses, and shows there is a link between them. 2. Separates items in a complex list.	On Tuesday, the bus was late; the train was early. You can go by aeroplane, train and taxi; Channel tunnel train, coach, then a short walk; or aeroplane and car.
'	**Apostrophe of possession** Denotes the ownership of one thing by another (see page 160).	This is Mona's scarf. These are the teachers' books.
'	**Apostrophe of contraction** Shows the omission of a letter(s) when two (or occasionally more) words are contracted.	Don't walk on the grass.
•••	**Ellipsis** 1. Shows the omission of words. 2. Indicates a pause.	The teacher moaned, 'Look at this floor… a mess… this class…' Lou said: 'I think I locked the door… no, hang on, did I?'
( )	**Brackets** Contains a parenthesis – a word or phrase added to a sentence to give a bit more information.	The cupboard (which had been in my family for years) was broken.
—	**Dash** 1. Indicates additional information, with more emphasis than a comma. 2. Indicates a pause, especially for effect at the end of a sentence. 3. Contains extra information (used instead of brackets).	She is a teacher – and a very good one too. We all know what to expect – the worst. You finished that job – and I don't know how – before the deadline.

Subject knowledge

Adding an apostrophe of possession

The addition of an apostrophe can create confusion. The main thing to look at is the noun – ask:

❑ Is it singular or plural?

❑ Does it end in an 's'?

If the noun is singular and doesn't end in 's', you add an apostrophe and an 's', for example: Indra's house the firefighter's bravery	If the noun is singular and ends in 's', you add an apostrophe and an 's', for example: the bus's wheels Thomas's pen
If the noun is plural and doesn't end in 's', you add an apostrophe and an 's', for example: the women's magazine the geese's flight	If the noun is plural and ends in 's', you add an apostrophe but don't add an 's', for example: the boys' clothes the dancers' performance

Further reading

Carter, R; Goddard, A; Reah, D; Sanger, K; Bowring, K (1997) *Working with Texts: A Core Book for Language Analysis*, Routledge

Crystal, D (1988) *Rediscover Grammar with David Crystal*, Longman

Crystal, D (1995) *The Cambridge Encyclopedia of the English Language*, Cambridge University Press
A big volume but very accessible, covering many areas of English including grammar, punctuation and dialect. Filled with interesting asides and examples from sources as varied as Shakespeare to Monty Python.

Hurford, R (1994) *Grammar: A student's guide*, Cambridge University Press
An excellent text, setting out basic guidelines on the workings of grammar.

Reah, D and Ross, A (1997) *Exploring Grammar: Main Routes and Scenic Paths*, WordsWork
A popular and accessible introductory course to grammar with interesting exercises to guide the reader.

Sealey, A (1996) *Learning About Language: Issues for Primary Teachers*, Open University Press
A more theoretical work that presents some of the issues and arguments surrounding knowledge about language.